# SAFER BY DESIGN

The management of product design risks under
strict liability

# SAFER BY DESIGN

The management of product design risks under
strict liability

Howard Abbott

THE
**DESIGN**
COUNCIL

First published 1987 in the United Kingdom by
The Design Council
28 Haymarket
London SW1Y 4SU

Typeset by Saxon Printing Limited, Saxon House, Derby

Printed and bound in Great Britain by
Biddles Ltd, Guildford and King's Lynn

British Library CIP Data

Abbott, Howard
  Safer by design: the management of
  product design risks under strict liability
  1. Product liability
  I. Title
  324.63'82      K953

ISBN 0 85072 204 7

# CONTENTS

# Tables

# Figures

# ACKNOWLEDGEMENTS

Special acknowledgement is made to Stuart Ashworth, Editor of *Product Liability International* and the *Product Liability Casebook*, for wise counsel and permission to include material from these publications.

I am grateful to many people for providing me with advice and comment. In particular I wish to thank Norman Farnworth of Leyland Vehicles, Greg Foster of Raychem Limited, Gordon Sanders of Stewart Wrightson, and the Consumers' Association, publishers of *Which?*

Howard Abbott
August 1987

# FOREWORD

This timely publication is the second book on product safety by Howard Abbott, author of *Safe Enough to Sell?* The concepts of strict liability for defective products and a general duty to supply safe products embodied in the Consumer Protection Act 1987 should prompt managers to take stock of their obligations under the law and see that they are properly equipped with policies, systems and expertise to cope.

Any company planning to stay in business wants to design, make and sell products that are safe. This may seem a self-evident proposition — but applying it in the highly competitive markets of the 1980s is anything but simple.

First, in the more mature economies, including the United Kingdom, firms have to depend more and more on new technology to give them a competitive edge in product specification, quality and price. Also, they have to bring their new products to market and then update them more quickly to keep ahead of the competition: the period between conceiving the product and putting it into the hand of the customer has been drastically shortened.

Next, even the smallest producer may be operating in a global market, buying or selling components all over the world. A knowledge of his liabilities for product defects both at home and abroad is essential and has to be matched by purchasing and sales records and insurance cover.

Finally, consumers are becoming more demanding in every sense: not only do they want the best products at the right price, but they are less and less willing to bear the risks which sometimes accompany the benefits of a high-tech world. Strict liability for producers absolves the injured consumer from the burden of showing that the manufacturer was negligent. Add to this the drive towards large-scale production, distribution and transportation and it becomes evident — as the case studies about the *Amoco Cadiz*, Flixborough, and the DC-10 cargo door in Howard Abbott's book amply demonstrate — that any defect in a product can generate potentially enormous claims for compensation.

How must business cope? First, it must do its level best to see that it operates within a legal regime that strikes a fair balance between the producer and consumer. Developments in the United States over the past 20 years — admittedly in a legal system that stimulates litigation — supply a horrible example, to put it bluntly, of what can happen if we get it wrong. Thus, there is now only one producer in the USA of a composite vaccine against common childhood ailments, because a small market and the threat of lawsuits has made others opt out. One British manufacturer of a sophisticated control and measuring device for anaesthetic equipment, although highly successful elsewhere, will not sell in America because of the risk of product liability claims. Society is obviously the poorer if it is denied the fruits of technical advance because producers and their insurers feel unable to shoulder the risk of a defect which even the most diligent search of relevant science and meticulous attention to design and testing fails to detect before the article is marketed. For this reason the CBI worked hard and long to secure the so-called developments risks defence in the EEC Directive, and the UK 1987 Act that embodies it.

But the real hard work has to go on in companies: in seeing that design takes full account of the safety factor from the use of materials right through to packaging and operating instructions: in assessing the risks arising in design, manufacture, distribution and maintenance and insuring against them.

*Safer by Design* is eminently practical in explaining the legal setting in which companies must operate and how to organise themselves to meet the challenge of safety and competition. Howard Abbott and the Design Council deserve our thanks for filling a pressing need.

John Banham, Director General, CBI
September 1987

# INTRODUCTION

People expect products to be safe, even though this has to be an unattainable absolute. Every product carries with it some risk, for someone, somewhere. But public awareness is changing as legislation makes greater provision to compensate those who suffer because of a defective product. When *Safe Enough To Sell?* was published in 1980 the idea of product safety as a function in its own right was new. Today, perceptive companies realise that not only is product safety a crucial activity, but also that it has to be managed if they are to maintain their place in the market. This new book is the result of much change in product safety since 1980, both in legislation and in management.

The biggest cause of product failure is probably design, especially as it can have an influence on the other sources: manufacturing error and failure to instruct or warn. When product failure results in death or injury, design may find itself quite literally on trial. This vulnerability of design will be increased by strict liability in tort, which the EEC Directive on Liability for Defective Products has brought to Europe.

The rules of the game are changed by strict liability. Any person injured by a defective product can recover compensation from the 'producer' without having to prove negligence. He or she will only have to show that when the 'producer' put the product into circulation it had a defect which caused the injury. This is in addition to all existing legislation and is a responsibility which cannot be excluded by contract.

The new concept will affect many cherished customs and practices. Familiar icons will need verification if they are to retain their privileged position. The idea of being able to make a 'safe' product will need re-examination. An immaculate claim-free past may not necessarily be a guide to the future, when the market risks will be different. The bulwark of insurance may be less stout than imagined. Throwing more money at the quality function may have a cosmetic effect, but not limit the exposure.

Even the lawyers cannot be relied upon to avoid the liability with a few deft clauses.

The contribution of design is fundamental to product safety if not, in many cases, the single most important factor. A fresh approach to design is required, when the penalty for getting it wrong can push a company over the threshold of ruin. In these circumstances design needs to be managed from a corporate point of view, and taken out of the cupboard under the stairs where it is usually kept.

Such management will require an input from the non-technical functions, as well as from those more usually associated with design. Contributions to the management strategy will come from those responsible for purchasing, insurance, legal aspects, finance, marketing and distribution, research and development, as well as from applications engineers, production engineers, quality assurance and the technical audit team.

The first part of this book briefly reviews the legal background to strict liability. Part 2 puts forward a strategy for the management of design risks. The book is *not* concerned with the engineering and scientific aspects of product safety, but rather with the way that these fit into the overall plan to make a safer product, remembering that a safe product is an unattainable absolute. The Case Histories tell of spectacular design calamities and also the way in which some companies have adopted a positive approach to ensure that their products are as safe as possible.

The management of product design risks concerns us all, in business and at home. In the research for this book the great reluctance of a wide range of companies and organisations to comment was evident. This applied in particular to those producing safety-critical products, who in fact could have made a valuable contribution.

Strict liability may make such companies realise that as society now demands safer products they should be prepared to demonstrate that they meet that demand.

# PART 1

# THE LEGAL BACKGROUND TO STRICT LIABILITY

# CHAPTER 1

## Product Liability in the United Kingdom

Product liability is not a new concept, neither is strict liability. Indeed, there has been strict liability in contract for a hundred years. This means that a seller is strictly liable to the purchaser of a product, but to no one else. If someone other than the purchaser suffers injury, that person has no contract with the seller, and so would have to bring an action in tort and prove negligence.

If a person suffers injury or damage because a product has a defective design there are two courses by which redress can be obtained: contract and tort. The circumstances of a particular incident will determine which is the best route for the victim to follow.

### CONTRACT

A contract for sale, which need not necessarily be in writing, in the course of business normally means that the goods must be of merchantable quality:

> Goods of any kind are of merchantable quality within the meaning of this Act if they are as fit for the purpose or purposes for which goods of that kind are commonly bought as it is reasonable to expect having regard to any description applied to them, the price (if relevant) and all the other relevant circumstances; and any reference in this Act to unmerchantable goods shall be construed accordingly.

This definition is from the Supply of Goods (Implied Terms) Act 1973 which was incorporated in the Sale of Goods Act 1979 Section 14 (6). It means that, for example, if a purchaser asks a seller for a spade, then the seller must provide a spade fit for the purpose for which spades are normally used. If the spade has a design defect, and thus is not of merchantable quality, it will not be fit for the purpose and the contract will have been broken. (See Case Histories 13 and 14.)

The Sale of Goods Act provides strict liability in contract, so that the purchaser of a spade with a design defect could succeed in an action for damages against the seller without having to show that he was negligent or otherwise at fault. This strict liability in contract is limited to the parties to the contract: the seller and the purchaser.

Contracts made in the course of business will have exclusion clauses and limitation clauses which will seek to limit liability, see Chapter 9. However, legislation makes void certain attempts to limit liability for death or personal injury, for example, see Unfair Contract Terms Act, page 9.

There are two aspects of contract that are important. The seller is strictly liable only to the purchaser, but not to anyone else who may have been injured by a defective product which he has sold. Such a person would have to bring an action under the tort of negligence, see below. The seller is strictly liable to the purchaser even though he may have sold the product as he received it from the distributor or manufacturer, without having had the opportunity or possessing the skill to examine it for defect.

## TORT

The second way in which a person injured by a product can recover damages is by the tort of negligence. The law of tort is concerned with the rights that one person has against other persons generally, whereas the law of contract is concerned with the rights and liabilities established by agreement between two or more parties. Tort is concerned with civil wrongs rather than criminal wrongs; the remedy for the former being compensation and for the latter imprisonment or a fine, although this distinction is no longer firm.

Under the tort of negligence a person harmed by a product can bring an action against anyone who was responsible for the defect in the product — but the plaintiff must prove negligence. Indeed, he has to prove three things, that:

— the product was defective,

— the defect caused the injury, and

— the defendant had failed in his duty of care.

It is the last of these which is frequently the most difficult to substantiate when the man in the street seeks to challenge a major company.

The duty of care was established in the famous snail-in-the-gingerbeer-bottle case, *Donoghue* v. *Stevenson* (1932)(AC 562). In a frequently quoted judgment Lord Atkin said

> A manufacturer of products, which he sells in such a form as to show that he intends them to reach the ultimate consumer in the form in which they left him with no reasonable possibility of intermediate examination, and with the knowledge that the absence of reasonable care in the preparation or putting up of the products will result in an injury to the consumer's life or property, owes a duty to the consumer to take that reasonable care.

The question of reasonable care was summed up by the Royal Commission on Civil Liability:

> It is a question of fact rather than law whether in all the circumstances of a particular case the nature of the defect raises a *prima facie* inference that there must have been some negligence in the design and manufacture of the article. The existence of a dangerous defect will often raise such an inference, and the manufacturer will then have the burden of proving the absence of negligence.[1]

## A REVIEW OF SOME RELEVANT ACTS

There can be no one Act that governs design. Laws and regulations are formulated by the Government to deal with a product in the hands of the user; frequently legislation appears after a disaster has drawn attention to a defect. Design criteria are usually the province of standards bodies, professional societies and trade associations. In certain cases safety regulations may be imposed on specific products by a Secretary of State under a relevant Act. A review of some of the Acts that can affect design must, therefore, be selective.

### Employers' Liability (Defective Equipment) Act 1969

If an employee suffers death or personal injury through a defect in equipment supplied, his employer is deemed to have been negligent. The liability is strict as it is not possible to exclude or limit any liability imposed by the Act. It is not enough, however, for the employee to suffer injury at work and plant or equipment to be involved. To come under the umbrella of the 1969 Act the employee must show that the defect in the equipment caused the accident. Section 1(1) states

> where...
>
> (a) an employee suffers personal injury in the course of his employment in consequence of a defect in equipment provided by his employer for the purposes of the employer's business;
>
> and
>
> (b) the defect is attributable wholly or partly to the fault of a third party (whether identified or not), the injury shall be deemed to be also attributable to negligence on the part of the employer (whether or not he is liable in respect of the injury apart from this sub-section), but without prejudice to the law relating to contributory negligence and to any remedy by way of contribution or in contract or otherwise which is available to the employer in respect of the injury.

The word 'equipment' includes any plant and machinery, vehicles, aircraft and clothing. By 'fault' is meant negligence, breach of statutory duty or other act or omission which gives rise to liability in tort. 'Personal injury' includes loss of life, any impairment of a person's physical or mental condition, and any disease.

The Employers' Liability (Compulsory Insurance) Act 1969 ensures that employers, other than governmental and local authority employers, must have insurance that will compensate employees injured by defective equipment, and that the insurance must be in the terms of an 'approved policy' as defined in the Act.

## Supply of Goods (Implied Terms) Act 1973

The equality of bargaining power assumed by the law of contract does not exist where the purchaser is an individual and the seller a multinational corporation. To meet this situation the 1973 Act substantially limited the power of vendors to avoid or restrict their liabilities; the Sale of Goods Act 1979 incorporates its provisions. The Unfair Contract Terms Act 1977, see page 9, also has a wide application to the sale of goods and hire purchase.

The Sale of Goods Act 1893 made it an implied term in a contract that goods should be of 'merchantable quality'. But the vital words were not defined until Supply of Goods (Implied Terms) Act 1973, see page 3, under Contract.

According to the 1893 Sale of Goods Act in Section 55, 'Where any right, duty or liability would arise under a contract of sale by implication of the law, it may be negatived or varied by express agreement.' In other words it was possible to contract out of the responsibility to supply goods of merchantable quality. Then the 1973 Act made void in the case of consumer sales any term exempting the provisions of Sections 13, 14 and 15 of the old Act. These are incorporated in the 1979 Act and deal with implied conditions in contracts of sale which are: that the goods correspond with their description; that the goods are merchantable; and that the goods are fit for the purpose for which they are sold. In other sales the term would not be enforceable 'to the extent that it is shown that it would not be fair or reasonable to allow reliance on it'.

In deciding whether an exclusion clause is fair or reasonable 'regard shall be had to all the circumstances of the case' and in particular:

— the relative strength of the parties' bargaining positions;

— whether the buyer 'received an inducement' to agree to the exclusion clause, or whether there was an alternative source of supply;

— whether the buyer 'knew or ought reasonably to have known' of the exclusion clause;

— if the seller's liability is conditional, whether the condition is reasonable; and

— whether the goods were supplied under a special order.

## Health and Safety at Work etc Act 1974

This Act provides a legislative framework for the protection of people at work and others affected by work processes. Every employer has the duty to ensure, so far as is reasonably practicable, the health, safety and welfare at work of all his employees. He must, so far as is reasonably practicable, make sure that the plant and systems are safe and without risks to health; that the use, handling, storage and transport of articles and substances are safe and without risk; that the necessary information, instruction, training and supervision are provided and that there are no risks involved with access to or egress from the working environment.

One of the principles of the Act is that industry should take responsibility for the health and safety of those people likely to be affected by its activities. The first link in this chain is Section 6, which aims to ensure that acceptable levels of health and safety are incorporated at the design and manufacturing stage.

This Section was revised by the Consumer Protection Act 1987, following a review of its powers of enforcement by the Health and Safety Commission, which took into account the White Paper, The Safety of Goods 1984 (Cmnd 9302). There is a provision that it is the duty of any person who designs, manufactures, imports or supplies any article for use at work, or any article of fairground equipment, to ensure, so far as is reasonably practicable, that the article is so designed and constructed that it will be safe and without risk to health at all times when it is being set, used, cleaned or maintained by a person at work.

The responsible person has to arrange for the carrying out of such testing and examination as may be necessary to ensure that the duty is met. He has to take the necessary steps that adequate information is supplied with the article so that it will be safe and without risk to health at the times mentioned above and when it is being dismantled or disposed of. He has to supply revisions of information should that become necessary by reason of something being known that could give rise to a serious risk to health or safety.

The phrase 'safe and without risks to health when properly used' includes the presumption that persons will act in the way they may reasonably be expected to behave, in circumstances which may reasonably be expected to occur. An article would not be properly used if no regard were taken of any relevant information or advice relating to its use made available by the designer, manufacturer, importer or supplier.

Finally, if the user chooses to disregard the information then it would be considered that there had not been proper use and the manufacturer would not be held liable for any harm caused.

## Unfair Contract Terms Act 1977

This Act was passed following the Law Commissions' Second Report on Exemption Clauses published in 1975, and it came into force on 1 February 1978. The principal aim of the Act is to invalidate or restrict attempts, by means of contractual terms or by notices, to exclude liability for negligence arising in the course of business.

The general rule is that liability for death or personal injury cannot be excluded. Liability for other loss or damage can only be excluded in so far as the contract term or notice satisfies, in view of the court, a reasonableness test. The general 'reasonableness' test is whether the term is a fair and reasonable one having regard to the circumstances which were, or ought reasonably to have been, known to or in the contemplation of the parties when the contract was made. In the case of an exclusion notice the test is whether it is fair and reasonable to allow reliance on it having regard to all the circumstances obtaining when the liability arises or (but for the notice) which would have arisen.

In all applications of the reasonableness test, the burden of showing reasonableness is on the person who is asserting that the clause should be upheld as reasonable. The provisions are very wide reaching covering sellers and hirers of goods, providers of services and some less obviously commercial activities. The Act applies to things done in the course of a business and is not restricted to the strictly commercial activities of businesses.

## Civil Liability (Contribution) Act 1978

This Act represented a considerable change in the position of those liable for an award for damages. Before the Act was passed a person held liable for damages could not recover any contribution towards the overall loss from another whose actions contributed. The Act makes provision for contribution by two or more persons held to be liable for the same award for damages.

Section 1 of the Act states

(1) Subject to the following provisions of this section, any person liable in respect of any damage suffered by another person may recover contribution from any other person liable in respect of the same damage (whether jointly with him or otherwise).

(2) A person shall be entitled to recover contribution by virtue of sub-section (1) above notwithstanding that he has ceased to be liable in respect of the damage in question since the time when the damage occurred, provided that he was so liable immediately before he made or was ordered or agreed to make payment in respect of 'which the contribution is sought'.

A person cannot, by way of contribution proceedings, be required to pay more than he would have been liable to pay if he had been sued directly by the plaintiff. A defendant's right to contribution is subject to a period of limitation of two years from the date on which it arose.

## Sale of Goods Act 1979

The law of the sale of goods was codified by an Act of Parliament passed in 1893 which was re-enacted as the Sale of Goods Act 1979. There have been many decisions in the courts in connection with the 1893 Act and, since the 1979 Act is virtually the same, these decisions still apply. It follows that any reading of the 1979 Act must be made in the knowledge of the cases decided since 1893.

The Sale of Goods Act lays certain duties on the seller such as those concerned with the delivery and ownership of the goods. Our specific interest is directed to the quality of goods, and here the goods must be of 'merchantable quality', if they are sold in the course of business, and they must be reasonably fit for their purpose.

Section 14 states:

(2) Where the seller sells goods in the course of a business, there is an implied condition that the goods supplied under the contract are of merchantable quality, except that there is no such condition

  (a)   as regards defects specifically drawn to the buyer's attention before the contract is made; or

(b) if the buyer examines the goods before the contract is made, as regards defects which that examination ought to reveal.

A definition of 'merchantable quality' from the Supply of Goods (Implied Terms) Act 1973 is repeated in Section 14 of the 1979 Act

(6) Goods of any kind are of merchantable quality within the meaning of subsection (2) above if they are as fit for the purpose or purposes for which goods of that kind are commonly bought as it is reasonable to expect having regard to any description applied to them, the price (if relevant) and all the other relevant circumstances.

In a consumer sale the seller cannot exclude his liability to supply goods that are of merchantable quality and are fit for their purpose. In a non-consumer sale, the seller must prove that any clause excluding these liabilities is reasonable.

The liability of the seller for defects in the goods he sells can be excluded by agreement, but it is subject to the Unfair Contract Terms Act 1977, see page 9. Section 55 of the 1979 Act states

(1) Where a right, duty or liability would arise under a contract of sale of goods by implication of law, it may (subject to the Unfair Contract Terms Act 1977) be negatived or varied by express agreement, or by the course of dealing between the parties, or by such usage as binds both parties to the contract.

See Case Histories 13 and 14.

## Limitation Act 1980

To bring or defend an action successfully a party has to call evidence. The cogency of evidence, particularly eye-witness evidence, obviously diminishes with the passage of time. Parties cannot be expected to keep documents which might be evidential for an indefinite period. Expert witnesses find difficulty in explaining, for example, what the state of knowledge of the art was years ago. It is inequitable for a potential claim to be hanging over the head of a defendant for an unconscionable period.

The law, recognising such problems, has developed periods of limitation so that even if all the essential elements of a successful claim are present an action will fail if it is not brought within the requisite time. It will be barred by reason of limitation.

The provisions of the Limitation Act 1980 include those whereby an action in tort or one founded on simple contract, or one to enforce an award must be brought within six years of the cause of the action accruing.

There are also provisions for sums recoverable by statute, actions in respect of wrongs causing personal injuries or death when the period is three years, actions to recover land and rent, and so on. In total the appropriate periods of limitation cover over 140 specific types of action or proceedings.

An important provision is to be found in Section 33, which is concerned with the discretionary exclusion of the time limit for actions in respect of personal injuries or death. If it appears to the court that it would be equitable to allow an action to proceed, the time limits provided for in the Act may be disregarded.

The time limit runs 'from the date on which the cause of action accrued' and in some cases this phrase has caused problems, especially when injury or damage does not become apparent until some time after it has been caused, which may happen, for instance, with some building defects.

## Consumer Protection Act 1987

For designers this is a significant watershed as it brings strict liability to the statute book. In a sentence it means that the manufacturer or importer of a product with a design defect will be liable to compensate a person who suffers damage, because of the defect, without him having to prove negligence.

However, the scope of the Act is considerably wider than that and deserves careful examination. There are five main areas:

Part I    Product liability. The implementation of the EEC Directive on Liability for Defective Products, see Chapter 3, is by this primary legislation rather than by Order under the European Communities Act 1972.

Part II     A general safety requirement for consumer goods following the proposals in the White Paper, The Safety of Goods 1984 (Cmnd 9302).

Part III     The introduction of an offence in giving to consumers misleading price indications about any goods, services, accommodation or facilities.

Part IV     A consolidation of the enforcement provisions taken from the Trade Description Act 1968, the Consumer Safety Act 1978 and the Consumer Safety (Amendment) Act 1986.

Part V     The main provision here amends the Heath & Safety at Work etc Act 1974 by improving the general duty on manufacturers to provide safe articles for use at work. Fairground equipment is brought within, the scope of the Act.

     There are a number of miscellaneous and supplemental provisions.

The Act received the Royal Assent on 15 May 1987. A summary of Part I is given below and is provided in full in Appendix 1.

     Each of the Member States of the Community has to introduce legislation to comply with the EEC Directive on Liability for Defective Products by July 1988. Part I of the Act is the United Kingdom's legislation to interpret the wording of the Directive, see Appendix.

     The principal provision is that any person who supplies a defective product will be liable for any damage that it causes. It will not be necessary to prove negligence to recover compensation. The remedy is in addition to all existing remedies in contract and tort.

     A product is defined as any goods, electricity, components that are part of a finished product and raw materials; game and agricultural produce (from the soil, stockfarming or fisheries) are excluded, unless they have undergone an industrial process.

     The Act places liability on four groups of people. Usually it will be the manufacturer who will be liable or, in the case of raw materials, the person who won or mined the product. Processors are only liable if they modify the essential characteristics of a product, although they may be liable as a supplier.

Importers are liable if they have imported a product into the Community in the course of their business and supplied it to someone else.

Own-branders are liable and are defined as persons who have held themselves out to be the producer of a product, by putting their name on the product, or using a trademark or other distinguishing mark in relation to a product.

Apart from manufacturers, importers and own-branders, a person who supplies a product will only be liable if he fails to identify the person who supplied him with the product.

Where two or more persons are liable for the same damage their liability is joint and several.

A product is held to be defective if its safety is not such as persons generally are entitled to expect. This includes the safety of components or raw materials comprised in another product. Safety is considered in the context of the risks of death, personal injury or damage to private property in excess of £275.

In determining the defectiveness of a product the following are taken into account: its marketing, instructions, warnings and get-up; what might reasonably be expected would be done with or in relation to the product; and the time the product was supplied by its producer to another. Defectiveness will not be inferred from the subsequent supply of a product safer than the one in question, or from the age of the product.

There are six defences available to the producer. He would have to prove:

— compliance with a requirement imposed by any Community obligation;

— that he did not supply the product;

— that the product was not supplied in the course of his business or for profit;

— that the defect did not exist in the product when he supplied it;

— that the state of scientific and technical knowledge at the time he supplied the product was such that no producer of such a product could have been expected to have discovered the defect;

— for a component or raw material, that the defect was wholly attributable to the design of the product in which it was comprised; or was due to compliance with the instructions given by the producer of the subsequent product.

Loss or damage is regarded as having occurred at the earliest time at which a person had knowledge of the material facts about the loss or damage. If the damage was caused partly by a defect in the product, and partly by the fault of the person suffering the damage, then his contributory negligence will be taken into account. Liability cannot be limited or excluded by any contract term, notice or other provision.

There is a cut-off of liability for the producer which operates ten years after he put a particular product into circulation. A person who suffers damage, as a result of a defective product, must bring an action within three years of the date on which the cause of the action occurred or he became aware of the damage. This part of the Act binds the Crown. Damage caused by nuclear accidents is excluded.

Part II of the Act provides that a person will be guilty of an offence if he supplies consumer goods which are not reasonably safe, having regard to all the circumstances. This is known as the general safety requirement. The definition of safety rests on that given in Part I; in addition it takes into account any safety standards or whether it would have been reasonable to have made the goods safer.

It will be a defence to show that a defect in the goods was due to compliance with a Community obligation. A person guilty of an offence will be liable to imprisonment, a fine or both. Part II also consolidates the Consumer Safety Act 1978 and the Consumer Safety (Amendment) Act 1986. This includes the powers to make regulations, which have been widened, and retains the powers for the Secretary of State to make prohibition notices and notices to warn, and empowers enforcement authorities to serve suspension notices.

Part III provides that there is a general offence of giving to consumers a misleading price indication about any goods, services, accommodation or facilities. The provision is supported by a Code of Practice.

Part IV is a consolidation of provisions concerned with enforcement, test purchases and powers of search and detention of goods.

Part V amends Part I of the Health & Safety at Work etc Act 1974. It improves the working of the general duty to provide safe articles and substances for use at work. The remainder of this part is concerned with some miscellaneous and supplemental provisions.

## THE POSITION OF THE DESIGNER

In simple terms a company must be reasonably careful in designing a product. Not only must the design be reasonably safe for the intended use, but it also should accommodate foreseeable misuse.

Unless there is a relevant contractual relationship, a person injured by a product with a defective design must show that the producer was negligent — that the latter failed to take reasonable care. The injured person must be able to satisfy the court that the defect made the product unreasonably dangerous, that the defect existed in the product when the producer put it into circulation, and that the product caused the injury.

To prove that a product was unreasonably dangerous, a plaintiff may well need expert witnesses and reference to the custom and practice of a particular industry. With a sophisticated product this may be difficult and expensive. If there are other factors present that led to the injury apart from the design defect, such as contributory negligence on the part of the injured party, then the potential liability of the producer will be affected.

The designer must take into account all those who may be affected by the product — that is, people other than the eventual user, such as distributors, installers, service engineers and even bystanders. The duty to take reasonable care extends to the duty to warn when the risk in a product may be hidden from the user. In sum the law today says

— if the injury was not reasonably foreseeable the designer cannot be liable;

— if the injury was reasonably foreseeable and was obvious to the user then the designer cannot be totally liable;

— if the injury was reasonably foreseeable and was hidden from the user but the designer took reasonable steps to

warn or protect the user then the designer cannot be totally liable;
but

— if the injury was reasonably foreseeable and was hidden from the user but the designer took no reasonable steps to warn the user then the designer is liable.

This is necessarily a simplified picture. Under strict liability in tort the injured person would not have to prove negligence on the part of the designer. This is the significant change introduced by the EEC Directive on Liability for Defective Products which is discussed in Chapter 3; its provisions were implemented by the Consumer Protection Act 1987. Under the Directive the injured person would only have to prove the defect, the injury and the causal link between the two. He would not have to satisfy the court that the designer failed to take reasonable care. (See Case Histories 13, 15 and 19.)

## SUMMARY

A person who is injured by a product with a defective design can seek redress through contract or tort. Between the purchaser and the seller there is strict liability in contract and negligence does not have to be proved. Under the tort of negligence any person harmed by a defective product can bring an action against anyone who is responsible for the defect — but he must prove negligence. A review of some of the relevant Acts reveals that certain clauses that could seek to exclude or limit liability are void. A designer is liable for an injury caused by his product if it was reasonably foreseeable, hidden from the user, and no reasonable steps were taken to warn the user. Strict liability in tort, introduced by the EEC Directive on Liability for Defective Products, and implemented by the Consumer Protection Act 1987, adds a new dimension to a designer's liability.

## REFERENCE

1    *Report of the Royal Commission on Civil Liability and Compensation for Personal Injury*. Cmnd 7054-I, p 258. London, HMSO, March 1978.

# CHAPTER 2

# Product Liability in Europe

## A REVIEW OF LEGISLATION IN SOME MAJOR COUNTRIES

Products that are not thought of as consumer products can still have a strong consumer orientation in some applications. For instance, a bearing can be found in an aircraft and a washing machine, a microchip in the computer control of a machine-tool and in a motor car, and software is used in space and in home information systems.

This chapter takes a look at the way different European countries try to protect their consumers. It is not intended to be a complete assessment of the legislative apparatus that would respond to a design failure, but rather to give a flavour of the variety of methods adopted.[1,2] The position in the United States is reviewed in Chapter 4.

The EEC Directive on Liability for Defective Products, see Chapter 3, will be adopted by Member States but not all in the same way. This gives an additional right of action to the victim of a design failure.

### Austria

The Federal Ministry for Family, Youth and Consumer Protection was created in 1983. The Product Safety Act came into force on 3 September 1983 with the aim of comprehensive protection against dangerous products by means of general standards, which can be applied where adequate protective measures are missing or insufficient. The Act established the Product Safety Advisory Board to prepare expert opinion, advise the Federal Minister and exchange data on dangerous products.

### Belgium

The basis on which current Belgian public health and protection policy rests is the Consumer Health Act 1977. It has put into effect the EEC Directive on Cosmetic Products; the toxicity of toys, pencils and crayons is also regulated under the Act. The Safety of Equipment Act 1961 applies to the safety of electrical apparatus, electrically operated toys and electrical installations in the home. The Dangerous Products Act 1980 is primarily aimed at protection in the work environment but extends to products used elsewhere. The Inspectorate-General for Consumer Policy, under the Ministry of Economic Affairs, is the administrative body responsible for consumer policy.

## Denmark

There is no general framework law on product safety. The Environmental Protection Act 1973 gives the Minister of the Environment powers to issue regulations prohibiting or limiting the importation or use of certain hazardous products; they have been used for the introduction of the EEC Directive on Cosmetic Products under the Cosmetic Products Order 1979. Potentially hazardous chemicals can be controlled under the Toxic and Hazardous Substances Act 1961. The lead and cadmium content of ceramics is restricted by the Ceramics Order 1972.

The production and storage of pesticides is controlled by the Pesticides Act 1961. The Marketing Practices Act 1974, *inter alia*, promotes the provision of adequate instructions and warnings. The Board of Approval and Registration of Electrical Equipment is authorised, under the Heavy Current Act 1977, to ensure that electrical products conform to the EEC Low Voltage Directive.

## France

France is very attached to written laws with penal regulation that can be used to punish any infringement. The passing of an important new Act was intended to change that basic approach to one of prevention. The Consumer Safety Act 1983 came into force on 22 January 1984 and provides for a general system of consumer safety. Under the Act there is a general obligation for manufacturers to produce safe products and services, although in fact this obligation already existed by virtue of case law.

The Act has three principles:

— Products and services shall under normal conditions

of use and other conditions reasonably foreseeable by the trader, meet legitimate expectations as to safety and not be prejudicial to health.

— From the first placing on the market, products must comply with the health and safety, fair trading and consumer protection regulations. The person responsible for first placing an article on the market shall therefore be obliged to check that it complies with the regulations in force. At the request of officials qualified to implement the present Act, he should provide proof that the requisite checks and inspection have been carried out.

— The Act provides that all parties concerned may both explain and defend their point of view when specific cases come up before the new Consumer Safety Commission.

The new Act, like the Protection and Information of Consumers Act 1978, gives the Government the general power to prohibit or regulate as far as necessary the production, import, offer, sale, free distribution, possession, labelling, packaging and utilisation of any products. The new Act adds to this the power to regulate or prohibit the export and circulation of products. All these powers are exercised by decrees made by the Government (*décret du Conseil d'Etat*) after advice from the newly created Consumer Safety Commission. The measures also apply to services.

The Government can order the withdrawal of products from the market and also order a producer to recall products for modification, exchange or total or partial refund. An order can be made for the destruction of products. Withdrawal or recall by decree only follows on advice from the Consumer Safety Commission. But the Minister of Consumer Affairs, or other Ministers, can order the withdrawal or recall of dangerous products by ministerial decree in cases of serious or immediate danger.

The Protection and Information of Consumers Act 1978 provides the general framework legislation, and gives Ministers the power to require certain products to satisfy regulations regarding their safe use. It also provides for powers to ban dangerous products. The Cosmetics Act 1975 incorporates the EEC Directive, and the Electrical Equipment (Safety) Act 1975 incorporates the EEC Low Voltage Directive. The Standards Act 1941 enables the Minister to make certain standards binding by decree.

### Germany

The Equipment Safety Act 1968, amended in 1979, lays down the safety requirements for all technical equipment displayed or marketed by a manufacturer or importer in the course of business; this includes household equipment and equipment for sports, hobbies and toys. The provisions of the Low Voltage Directive were incorporated by decree in 1979.

The Foodstuffs and Commodities Act 1974 has as its main objective the protection of the health and safety of the consumer. Cosmetics have to satisfy the requirements of the EEC Directive and toys come under the Equipment Safety Act 1968. A competent authority in each *Land* (or State) enforces the provisions of the Act, and there is a general prohibition on commodities that do not satisfy the legal requirements. In cases of emergency the Federal Minister can ban the sale of a product he considers to be dangerous.

### The Netherlands[3]

A number of ministries have general or specific responsibility for home safety policy. The Ministry of Housing, Physical Planning and Environment supervises the safety of buildings and the Ministry of Home Affairs is concerned with fire prevention. The Ministry of Economic Affairs bears responsibility for the safety of gas and electrical appliances. The Ministry of Welfare, Health and Cultural Affairs has general responsibility for safety in the home, and is specifically responsible for safety in respect of sports and leisure activities, pesticides, and consumer products.

Specific product safety regulations for certain categories may be promulgated to supplement the Commodities Act 1935. Examples are decrees concerning toys, lifejackets, fireworks, cosmetics, products containing asbestos and soft drink bottles (because of the risk of explosion). The Electricity Decree (or Order), made under the Electricity Act, is the Dutch version of the EEC Low Voltage Directive. The Cosmetic Decree follows the EEC Directive.

The Product Safety Department of the Ministry of Welfare, Health and Cultural Affairs is charged with drawing up safety regulations; it is advised on this by the State Health Inspectorate and the Advisory Committee on the Commodities Act. The Consumer Safety Institute was established in 1983.

## Ireland

There is no framework Consumer Safety Act. The Industrial Research and Standards Act 1961, Section 44, enables the Minister for Industry and Commerce to issue Safety Orders requiring particular goods to comply with specifications, including those in Irish standards; for example, all toys must satisfy the relevant Irish Standard Specification regarding toxicity and cellulose content. EEC Directives are enacted in their entirety by regulations and by modifying existing requirements; for example, the Directives on Dangerous Substances, Paints etc, Electrical Equipment and Cosmetics have all been enacted in this way.

The Sale of Goods and Supply of Services Act 1980 provides for implied terms and conditions which ensure that a purchaser can expect goods to be of 'merchantable quality', 'fit for their purpose', and as described. It is similar to the UK Sale of Goods Act 1979.

The Consumer Information Act 1978 prohibits, under certain circumstances, false or misleading indications about goods, services and prices given in the course of a business, trade or· profession. It is similar to the UK Trade Descriptions Act 1968.

## Italy[4]

Legislation does not protect the consumer against damage, loss or injury caused by product defect. The liability of the manufacturer, wholesaler or retailer for such occurrences can only arise from contractual provisions and clauses, or the evidence of fault and negligence in manufacturing the product. Italian laws are still based on liability in tort criteria, although some judges now tend to follow criteria closer to strict liability, at least as far as the burden of proof is concerned.

With the exception of foodstuffs and health legislation, there are very few consumer laws in Italy. The Electrical Equipment Safety Act 1977 (No 791) implements the EEC Low

Voltage Directive and is the responsibility of the Minister for Industry and Commerce.

The concept of strict liability for product defects is not familiar to the vast majority of Italian people. The idea about the right to be indemnified is closely connected to those of 'fault' or 'negligence', where the cause/effect relationship with loss or injury must be proved by the plaintiff.

## Portugal

The Consumer Protection Act 1981 was followed by the definition, in 1983, of the functions of the Ministry for the Quality of Life (MQV):

> 'The living standard of the population also involves consumer protection in the broadest sense and includes the protection of those at whom advertising is directed. It is therefore logical that the Ministry for the Quality of Life should be the government department responsible, in co-ordination with other government departments, for effectively developing an extended and coherent policy to safeguard the legitimate rights and interests of the consumers.'

The MQV has to safeguard the rights and interests of the consumer and to help in the formulation and approval of Portugese regulations to protect consumers. To help in this task there is the Consumer Protection Bureau and National Consumer Protection Institute.

## Spain

The Health and Consumer Action Unit is responsible for taking preventative action where a genuine risk occurs and co-ordinates resources and administration. It deals with crisis situations and emergencies. An Interministerial Commission was created in 1983 to co-ordinate and administer the inspection services for durable and consumer goods and services.

## SUMMARY

European countries vary in the methods by which they seek to help to protect consumers from the consequences of product failure. France has an Act that puts a general obligation on manufacturers to produce safe products and the United Kingdom has moved in the same direction. By contrast, Denmark has no general framework law on product safety and neither has Ireland, while in Italy the liability of the manufacturer can only arise from contractual provisions or evidence of fault or negligence. Certain countries, Austria for instance, are following the standards route, a few have mandatory recall, and others have established special bodies with powers to protect the consumer.

## REFERENCES

1   *Consumer Policy in OECD countries* (1985). Paris, Organization for Economic Co-operation and Development.
2   Jenkins, D W (1982) *Controlling the Safety of Consumer Products in the European Economic Community*. London, Institute of Trading Standards Administration.
3   Tebbens, H D (1981) Dutch Product Liability Law *Product Liability International*. Colchester, Lloyd's of London Press.
4   Savio, C (1982) Conference Report Product Liability in Italy. *Product Liability International*. Colchester, Lloyd's of London Press.

# CHAPTER 3

# EEC Directive on Liability for Defective Products

## STRICT LIABILITY IN TORT

The effect of the Directive is to add strict liability in tort to the laws of the Member States. This means that a person who suffers damage because of a defective product can succeed in an action against its producer without having to prove that he was negligent. It is the absence of the need to prove negligence that has caused so much debate. Strict liability is not new in the United Kingdom, where there has been strict liability in contract since the last century, see Chapter 1. Other European countries, not members of the EEC, may follow the provisions of the Directive in due course.

The Member States will not necessarily all change their individual laws in the same way to adopt the provisions of the Directive. Apart from the three derogations discussed in this chapter, differences in emphasis will become apparent, as will differences in interpretation. Until each Member State has passed into its legislation a 'Product Liability Act', and there has been time to evaluate them, it will not be possible to assess the detailed effect of the Directive. The United Kingdom implemented the Directive by means of the Consumer Protection Act 1987, see Chapter 1.

The following summary of its provisions should be read with the above comments in mind. The Directive appears in full in Appendix 2.

## SUMMARY OF THE PROVISIONS

The principle of strict liability is laid down in Article 1: 'The producer shall be liable for damage caused by a defect in his product'. The two words that need explanation are 'producer' and 'product'.

A 'product' is defined as a movable, even though it is incorporated into another movable or into an immovable. As a product is tangible property, other than land and buildings, the scope of the Directive is not restricted to consumer products, as is sometimes thought. The Directive will apply to building material producers but not to the work of building and civil engineering contractors; a brick would be classed as a movable but not the work of the civil engineer that put it into its final position. 'Product' includes electricity, but is more concerned with its generation than defects occurring after electricity has been put into the grid.

Primary agricultural products and game are excepted from the scope of 'product'. These are the products of the soil, stock farming and fisheries, but excluding products which have undergone initial processing. Member States can withdraw this exemption because Article 15 allows that, by way of derogation from Article 2, any Member State may include primary agricultural products and game within the scope of its legislation.

The word 'producer' means manufacturer, importer or own-label supplier. It includes the manufacturer of a finished product or component, the producer of raw material and the person who holds himself out to be the producer by putting an own brand label on a product. In the case of a product manufactured outside the EEC the importer will be liable.

Where the producer of a product cannot be identified, each supplier of the product will be treated as its producer, unless he informs the injured person (within a reasonable time) of the identity of the producer or of the person who supplied him with the product. This applies in the case of an imported product so that, even if the name of the producer (outside the EEC) is displayed, the identity of the importer must be indicated. Any person in the chain of supply, including the retailer, is liable unless he can show who supplied the product to him.

The injured person has to show the damage, the defect and the causal relationship between them, but importantly he does not have to prove negligence.

Where two or more people are liable for the same damage they will be liable jointly and severally but existing rights of contribution or recourse are not affected. The Civil Liability (Contribution) Act 1978 is applicable here, see Chapter 1.

The definition of a defective product is found in Article 6. This states, 'A product is defective when it does not provide the safety which a person is entitled to expect, taking all circumstances into account....' This is, to all intents and purposes, all that a designer will get as a definition of the degree of safety he is expected to incorporate in his product. The Article goes on to enumerate the circumstances which have to be taken into account.

The first is the presentation of the product which includes instructions, labelling, advertising, marketing claims, warnings, labels and so on. The effect is that the product, *per se*, cannot be looked at in isolation. From a product liability point of view all the communications made regarding the product have to be taken into account as well. For the designer one of the most important aspects will be instructions and warnings. The second circumstance is 'the use to which it could reasonably be expected that the product would be put'. Buried in this sentence is the need for the designer to take into account foreseeable misuse, but not a use for which the product was clearly not intended, for instance, using a hover mower to cut a hedge. The third circumstance is 'the time when the product was put into circulation'. This is particularly important when we come to consider the state of the art defence and the ten year cut-off (see page 30). A product will not be considered defective for the sole reason that a better product is subsequently put into circulation.

The producer has six so-called defences, with in each case the burden of proof resting on the producer. If the producer did not put the product into circulation, that is when it has been delivered to another person in the course of business, he will not be liable. He will also escape liability if he can show that the defect did not exist when he put the product into circulation; or that the product was not manufactured for an economic purpose or distributed in the course of his business. Compliance with mandatory regulations issued by public authorities would be a defence, if the producer could show that the defect was the inevitable result of compliance.

The development risks defence has caused more debate than any other point in the Directive. This defence provides that if the producer can show that the state of scientific and technical knowledge, at the time when he put the product into circulation, was not such as to enable the existence of the defect to be discovered then he will not be liable. This is the second derogation. Article 15 provides that each Member State may exclude the development risks defence, either in its entirety or in whichever sector or sectors are considered necessary.

The producer of a component will not be liable if he can prove that the defect was attributable either to the design of the product in which the component had been fitted, or to the instructions given by the manufacturer of the product. This means that suppliers of components made to the specification of the manufacturer of the final product will not be liable, if the defect was the inevitable result of compliance. In such a case it is the final product manufacturer who is liable.

The liability of the producer may be reduced in the event of contributory negligence on the part of the injured person. The scope of 'damage' in Article 1 means death or personal injuries and also damage to or destruction of private property with a value of more than 500 ECUs. There is a limitation period of three years for the bringing of proceedings which starts to run from the day on which the plaintiff became aware, or should reasonable have become aware, of the damage, the defect, and the identity of the producer. Ten years from the date on which the producer put the product into circulation his liability under the Directive ends, unless an injured person has in the meantime started proceedings against him.

Article 12 prevents a producer from limiting or excluding his liability under the Directive by contract or any other form of agreement. Further, the Directive does not affect any rights which an injured person may have under the laws of contract and tort, therefore the Directive's provisions are in addition to all existing legislation. Injury or damage arising from nuclear accidents is exempted.

The third derogation concerns a financial limit which must be not less than 70 million ECUs. The provision is that the total liability for damage resulting from a death or personal injury caused by identical items with the same defect shall not exceed the limit given. The effect of this provision will be reviewed in 1995. The Directive does not apply to products put into circulation before the date on which the provisions come into force, which must be not later than July 1988. Every five years the Commission will present a report to the Council on the application of the Directive.

## THE IMPACT ON DESIGN

The definition of a 'product' as a movable gives the provisions of the Directive a particularly wide application. 'Producer' takes in manufacturers of end-products, raw materials and components as well as those who supply own-label products. The exclusion of the need to prove negligence, which is the basis of strict liability in tort, means that the designer's exposure increases considerably, as an injured person only has to prove the damage, the defect and the casual relationship between the two.

The degree of safety which a designer must incorporate into a product is that which a person is entitled to expect, taking all the circumstances into account. To turn this lawyer's definition into an engineering reality will require a fresh approach to the design function, see Part 2.

As the presentation of the product is taken into account when deciding on defectiveness, designers will have to be particularly careful about all the words and illustrations that accompany a product, see Case Histories 14 and 15. One of the more difficult areas will be foreseeable misuse, because producers will be liable for a use to which a product could reasonably be expected to be put. People use products in ways which a designer never intended, but if such a use is known and no warnings are given to prevent such use which may be dangerous, then the designer will have some liability.

Record keeping will become critical. The time when a product is put into circulation is taken into account in considering its defectiveness. This is important if the development risks defence were to be used in a product liability incident. If this defence is allowed in a Member State, then it may be that the designer could show that, at the time the product was put into circulation, the state of science and technology was such that he could not have discovered the defect. The background to safety-critical design decisions will need to be recorded, together with the reasons for choosing one method rather than another. The design review system (see Chapter 8) will need to be carefully logged.

Records could be equally important to support a defence that a product was not defective when it was put into circulation. In effect, this would mean that the producer was demonstrating that someone downstream of him had to be responsible for the defect arising.

Compliance with mandatory regulations and standards may not prove to be the straightforward defence that it would appear at first sight. It is important to realise that it is only regulations and standards that have the force of law that have application here, and very many do not. Often standards are concerned with performance and measurement and have little or nothing to do with safety. To use this defence the designer would have to be able to demonstrate that, in effect, the standard itself was defective because he could escape liability by demonstrating that it was the inevitable compliance with the standard which caused the damage.

The component designer will have to be clear where his responsibility ends and that of the end-product manufacturer begins. If it can be shown that the component supplier contributed in some way to the end-product's design, then some responsibility for liability could follow a product incident, if the component was associated with it.

## SUMMARY

The effect of the EEC Directive on Liability for Defective Products is to add to the laws of the Member States strict liability in tort. This means that a person who suffers damage from a defective product can succeed in an action against the producer without having to prove negligence. A product is defined as a movable, and a producer is a manufacturer, importer or own-label supplier. There are six so-called defences available to a producer, with the burden of proof shifted on to him. A producer cannot limit or exclude his liability, but it may be reduced by contributory negligence on the part of the injured person. The degree of safety which a designer must incorporate in a product is that which a person is entitled to expect, taking all the circumstances into account. This new ruling will require a fresh approach to the design function.

# CHAPTER 4

## Product Liability in the United States

### STRICT LIABILITY IN TORT

It was in 1963 that the concept of strict liability arrived in the United States, or rather that is the date generally accepted because of a decision in the California Supreme Court. Before that year actions for injuries caused by defective products had been based on either breach of warranty or negligence. After 1963 there was the additional choice of basing an action on strict liability in tort.

The case in question was *Greenman* v. *Yuba Power Products Inc*, and the Court held that a 'manufacturer is strictly liable in tort when an article he places on the market, knowing that it is to be used without inspection for defects, proves to have a defect that causes an injury to a human being'. The case is of particular interest from a design point of view, because Mr Greenman presented substantial evidence to show that his injuries were the result of defective design and construction. (See Case History 15.)

### INSURANCE CRISIS

The impact of strict liability on the United States was significant. It led to what was described as the product liability crisis. In 1975 a number of manufacturers and business publications claimed that the situation had become so bad that product liability insurance was either unobtainable or unaffordable. The White House set up a special body to investigate the problem. The Federal Interagency Task Force on Product Liability reported in January 1977 after a year of intensive study. The Task Force found there was no widespread difficulty in obtaining product liability insurance, but in certain industries with high-risk product lines there was difficulty in obtaining cover, while for others premiums did appear to be unaffordable. The average cost of product liability insurance was less than one per cent of sales in the target industries, but was higher for some manufacturers. The total cost of product liability could be higher than one per cent, because distributors and retailers could pass on the cost of their product liability insurance.

The section of the report dealing with Product Liability Loss Prevention is of importance in considering design for product safety. It says

> The tort-litigation system and increased product liability insurance costs have caused many manufacturers of high-risk products to devote more time and resources to product liability loss prevention; however, a number of such businesses have not done so. Limited data show that a much higher percentage of large, as opposed to small, manufacturers have implemented product liability loss prevention programs. Also, insurers appear to have supplied product liaibility advice more frequently to large insurers than to small ones. In addition, company executives interviewed by the industry contractor did not perceive a direct correlation between the implementation of product liability loss prevention programs and a reduction in insurance costs.[1]

## JUDICIAL SYSTEMS

Much of the European alarm at strict liability has been generated by stories about its effect in the United States.

One of the most significant factors is that the judiciary in the United States is different from that found in the United Kingdom and the rest of Europe. The seemingly unusual verdicts and high damages are frequently a product of the United States judicial system rather than of strict liability itself. There are two systems in the United States, the Federal Judicial System and the State Judicial System, with no two states being identical.

The judges of the Federal Courts are appointed by the President with the approval of Congress. Almost all Federal litigation starts in a US District Court and there is one or more for each state. The District Courts are grouped into eleven circuits, each with its own Court of Appeals. The District Courts try both civil and criminal cases and sit as bankruptcy and admiralty courts. Appeals from one of the eleven Courts of Appeals go to the US Supreme Court in Washington, DC.

Each state has a Court of First Instance, although its name varies from state to state. There may be an Intermediate Appellate Court but always an Appeals Court, which is the court of last resort unless a Federal question is involved. In State Courts the judges are elected by popular vote or appointed by the Governor of the state.

Each part of the dual judicial system has its own exclusive jurisdiction. Federal Courts, for instance, deal exclusively with patents, copyrights and trade marks. State Courts deal exclusively with probate, matrimonial and domestic relations. The jurisdiction of a Federal District Court includes cases where the sum involved is over $10 000 and there is a diversity of citizenship (the plaintiff and the defendant come from different states). As one or other of these requirements is easily met in most product liability cases it is the Federal Courts that often try them. Such a court will apply the law of the state in which it is sitting, and the product liability law varies from state to state. However, the plaintiff may be able to bring his action in the State Judicial System rather than in the Federal one and sue in a State Court.

Apart from the judiciary, there are other important differences between the American legal system and that in the United Kingdom.

— The US Constitution protects the injured person's right to trial by jury. If damages are to be awarded it is the jury that determines the amount.

— The unsuccessful litigant does not have to pay the fees of his lawyer. The successful litigant may pay his lawyer about one third of the judgment award. This is called the contingency fee system.

— Because of the concurrent jurisdiction of the Federal and the State Courts the plaintiff may have the option of bringing his case in more than one court. If his lawyer seeks the court which offers him the greatest chance of success it is called forum shopping.

— Most states have specific statutes that enable steps to be taken to obtain jurisdiction when there is only minimal contact between, say, a foreign party and a State Court. These are called long-arm statutes.

— There is a tendency to bring an action against the party which seems most likely to pay. This is the deep-pocket theory.

— Punitive damages can be awarded in certain cases. This can lead to multi-million dollar awards.

— There are no social security schemes in the United States, a factor taken into account by juries when assessing damages.

— The Freedom of Information Act gives a plaintiff access to information that would be denied to him in the United Kingdom.

## FEDERAL LEGISLATION

The Federal Interagency Task Force on Product Liability identified uncertainty in product liability law as the major problem. In January 1979 the Department of Commerce published a draft of a model Uniform Product Liability Act and asked for comments. Since then a number of attempts have been made to introduce a Federal Act but none has succeeded in reaching the statute book. Thus, each state has its own product liability legislation which will apply to cases heard within its jurisdiction.

## DESIGN CASES

There is little to be gained in rehearsing the many stories that circulate regarding instances of apparent lunacy in product liability cases in the United States. Some stories belong to the Apocrypha like the poodle in the microwave oven. However, it is instructive to examine landmark cases concerned with design, to gain an idea of how design defects are judged in one regime of strict liability. (See Case Histories 15, 16, 17 and 18.)

## SUMMARY

The United States has two judicial systems, the Federal and the State, which operate alongside each other. There are other significant differences in the legal climate which make a meaningful comparison with Europe unrewarding. Strict liability in tort began in 1963 but its implementation is not uniform throughout the United States because each State has its own jurisdiction. Attempts to establish a Uniform Product Liability Act, in one form or another, have failed so far.

## REFERENCE

1    *Executive Summary of the Interagency Task Force on Product Liability*, pp 265-450. NTIS, January 1977.

# PART 2

# THE MANAGEMENT OF DESIGN RISKS

# CHAPTER 5

## The Management Strategy

### SAFETY IN DESIGN IS A MANAGEMENT RESPONSIBILITY

Strict liability in Europe gives design a new dimension. Too much is at stake to leave the responsibility for design in the hands of one department, let alone one man. The cost of some design defects has been formidable as the Case Histories show only too well. The *Amoco Cadiz*, the Brent Cross mobile crane, the DC-10 cargo door, and the Tay Bridge all had design defects which either killed or injured many people. (See Case Histories 1, 6, 8 and 20.)

It is this simple word 'defect' that creates difficulty. What it means, exactly what it means, depends on the training and education one has received. Broadly, there is a dichotomy between the lawyers on the one hand and the engineers on the other. A lawyer needs a definition like a suitcase that can be expanded or contracted to suit every circumstance. This is because he cannot know all the situations in which it may be used; he needs a catch-all to cover a microchip, a bus, a tin of beans or a teddy bear.

Article 6 of the EEC Directive on Liability for Defective Products states that a product is defective when, 'it does not provide the safety which a person is entitled to expect, taking all circumstances into account', see Chapter 3. It is proposed to amend the Consumer Safety Act by placing a general duty on all suppliers to ensure that the goods they supply are safe, in accordance with sound modern standards of safety. The latter would be defined in terms of the standard of reasonable safety a person is entitled to expect, bearing in mind considerations such as cost and the state of the art.

Section 6 of the Health and Safety at Work Act imposes on designers a duty to ensure, so far as is reasonably practicable, that articles and substances for use at work are safe and without risks to health when properly used, see Chapter 1.

The Sale of Goods Act 1979 imposes 'merchantable quality' on all goods sold under contract, which means that the goods are as fit for the purpose for which goods of that kind are commonly bought as it is reasonable to expect them to be having regard to the relevant circumstances, see Chapter 1.

However, a designer will find these definitions difficult to turn into practice, as they are open to interpretation.

Superlatives and comparatives by themselves have no value to the designer. They have to relate to something specific to gain perspective. Expressions such as 'Best quality', 'Highest standard' and 'Largest capacity' have no real meaning, unless they refer to graduated degrees of quality, standards or capacities. Similarly, 'Guaranteed 100 per cent pure', 'No deleterious substances present', 'No danger when used according to the instructions' or 'Completely safe for children' are all impossible absolutes.

The claim 'Guaranteed 100 per cent pure' gives no benchmark by which the purity has been measured, nor does it specify the quantity which is claimed to be pure. Is it 10 tonnes, a milligram or one tested sample? 'No deleterious substances present' might mean that the manufacturer did not find any in the sample he tested. In the 1980s can any responsible designer claim: 'No danger when used according to the instructions'? Instructions and warnings have to be comprehensible to the man on the Clapham omnibus. They have to be in his language and not call for a university degree to understand them. A manufacturer has a duty to make sure that his instructions and warnings are heard by the end-user.

'Completely safe for children', like the previous claims, carries with it the unattainable aura of omniscience. Is it safe when used in the pouring rain, in an aircraft, with a cat on the lap or when riding a bicycle? This kind of phrase, and the others, is of no use to the designer because in the true sense it cannot be achieved. It would be foolish to protest that a product was 'Completely safe for children' because the company had never had a complaint. Just one complaint, next Friday afternoon, would destroy the whole claim.

The criteria for safety involve social, political and technical judgements. One expert[1] has suggested that if a risk is so low that only one person in 10 million were killed every year then action to reduce it further is not justified. The choice of this figure is based on the fact that risks of this level (lightning, falling aircraft, snake and insect bites), are considered so low by almost everyone that action to reduce them further would be considered almost absurd.

If we accept this view then we are saying that we cannot avoid every conceivable accident; which means that numerical methods should be used to decide what level of risk to accept. In fact, we are saying we have to decide how 'safe' a product should be. Some hazards should be eliminated because their risks are too high, while others should be reduced to the minimum. But what is the minimum?

The definitions of safety given above start to get difficult to interpret when they are translated into the value of a human life. This takes us into social and political areas which are beyond the scope of this book, although attempts have been made to quantify the value of a life. A recent survey[2] put the figure at between £1 million and £2 million.

For occupational safety and health in industry a target can be set against an agreed scale. For example, the Fatal Accident Frequency Rate (FAFR) is the number of fatal accidents in a group of 1000 men in a working lifetime of 100 million hours.

Table 1 *FAFR values for various UK industries*

| | |
|---|---|
| Clothing and footwear | 0.15 |
| Vehicles | 1.30 |
| Chemical industry | 4.00 |
| British industry (ie all premises covered by the Factories Acts) | 4.00 |
| Metal manufacture and shipbuilding | 8.00 |
| Agriculture | 10.00 |
| Fishing | 36.00 |
| Coal Mining | 14.00 |
| Railway shunters | 45.00 |
| Construction erectors | 67.00 |

*Source:* Kletz, T A (1980) Benefits and risks: their assessment in relation to human needs. *Endeavour* NS 4 (2): pp 46-51.

A target can be set for a man doing a specified job that he should not be exposed to a FAFR of more than, say, two. The risks have to be brought within this limit by eliminating some and reducing others. Another example of the quantification of safety was an Air Registration Board requirement that an automatic landing system should have a probability of a fatal landing of not more than 1 in 10 million.

For many products this approach would be very difficult because of the lack of data and the resources to obtain them. The complexities of some common products increase apace without failure rates being known. Software introduces its own problems as it is impossible to check that a computer program is completely reliable and safe. And yet there is an increasing demand to supply safer products within commercially acceptable cost parameters.

For the majority of products, then, we cannot set a finite safety target nor can we use a phrase such as 'completely safe'. The alternative is to establish a programme which will make a product as safe as possible, by using a balanced approach which accepts the realities of product safety in a pragmatic way.

## SOURCES OF DEFECT

There are three sources of a product failure:

— design defect

— manufacturing error

— failure to warn

(See Case Histories 13, 14 and 19.)

We are only concerned with the first, which is perhaps the major source of product failure, bearing in mind that it can have a major influence on the other two. The need to manage safety in product design is clear and what follows is the outline of a course to achieve that end.

To do this effectively a strategy is needed to provide a framework which ensures that the company's requirements are met. It establishes the infrastructure to direct the tactics which will manage the potential product design exposures. There can be no fixed rules, for each company has a unique combination of products, people and markets.

However, we will examine the more common factors, remembering that they have to be in place for some time before they can influence the course of events.

It will be seen that the management of safety in product design includes functions other than those normally associated with design. The need for this wider contribution is a reflection of the wider consequences of a design failure in a regime of strict liability. The techniques of yesterday will need modification to be effective in the new situation.

## KEY ELEMENTS OF STRATEGY

The four key elements of the strategy are briefly reviewed below, before being examined in detail in the subsequent chapters.

1    Identify the product risks. If the risks have not been identified they cannot be managed. The danger is that managers familiar with the product will assume that they already know its hazards and the risks they present. But that very familiarity is a hazard because, as we have seen in Part 1, the climate of risk has changed. The market-place in which the product is sold will take on a new dimension with the introduction of strict liability, so a fresh approach to the whole question of risk identification is required.

2    Risk reduction programme. The next element of the strategy is active risk reduction, possibly as part of a design review system. As this programme develops some of the risk identification techniques may be used to help evaluate the success of the risk reduction activity.

3    Risk transfer programme. As no product can be absolutely safe, any risk reduction programme will leave residual product risks. Some of these, once they have been identified, can be transferred to third parties by such mechanisms as insurance or contract.

4    Risk retention programme. However successful the previous elements of the strategy, some residual product risk will have to be retained within the company. An active programme will provide more protection than a passive one.

The strategy follows classic risk management principles, applied to a special requirement. There is a further element, risk avoidance, which is not considered in this book. An example would be a product for use in a hostile environment which had to reduce to the minimum the possibility of a spark; one way of achieving this would be to avoid the risk of an electric spark by using a hydraulic form of energy. Another way of avoiding risk would be to stop making a product which had too many risks associated with it. Risk avoidance is more of a negative concept in product safety than it is in other risk management applications, such as occupational safety and health in the chemical industry. It is assumed that risk avoidance is folded into risk reduction for product safety.

## SUMMARY

No product can be absolutely safe and some industries set safety targets against an agreed scale. Achieving an acceptable degree of product safety requires a strategy to manage design, as this is probably the major source of product failures. Given the lack of failure data for many products, it is proposed that the strategy should have four elements: risk identification, risk reduction, risk transfer and risk retention.

## REFERENCES

1    Kletz, T A (1982) Hazard analysis — a review of criteria. *Reliability Engineering* 3 (4): pp 325-38.
2    Jones-Lee, M (1985) The value of safety: results of a National Sample Survey. *The Economic Journal* pp 1-24.

# CHAPTER 6

# IDENTIFICATION OF RISKS 1
## Data on Accidents Involving
## Consumer Products

## THE LACK OF INFORMATION

Surprisingly, there are few data on which products are most likely to injure someone. Designers would be the first to benefit from a data bank that could warn them of those products which required the greatest attention from a safety point of view. Even more important would be a source of information that could reveal why a particular product caused an accident. In some industries with sensitive products, leading companies have computerised systems to provide them with an early warning system to detect patterns of failures and defects. Motor manufacturers have this type of facility as part of the back-up for a product recall. In a similar way pharmaceutical companies have a detection system, although they appear to be wondrously shy about letting anyone know about it. Insurers and brokers may have some data on which products cause harm and why, but it is probably much more meagre than many realise. Comparative guide rates for product liability insurance premiums give a vague wave in the general direction of which products cause harm, but no more than that, see Chapter 9.

Statistics on product-related accidents are rare indeed. The Pearson Commission said

> There are no published statistics, but our personal injury survey suggests that between 30 000 and 40 000 injuries a year (about one per cent of all injuries) may be caused by defective products including drugs. Of these, something over 10 000 occur during the course of work, and a further 10 000 involve services as well as defective products.[1]

It was estimated that about five per cent of the 30 000 to 40 000 injuries would attract compensation through either tort or contract.

The average amount paid was £500, which was half the average for tort compensation as a whole. Claims in respect of liability for products and services represented about one per cent of all claims on insurers, but accounted for only 0.3 per cent of business in the courts. There was evidence to suggest that claims involving product liability tended to be disposed of at an earlier stage than other claims.

The Commission reported that its estimates did not give a complete picture because they gave no indication of the growing nature of the problem. 'Product liability risks may be comparatively few in number, but the range of risk extends from minor harm to major catastrophe.' Nowhere does the report examine which products cause harm or why.

## UNITED KINGDOM

A feasibility study to test methods of collecting information on product-related accidents was begun in 1973-74 by the Home Office, which was then responsible for consumer safety. The study showed that the accident and emergency departments of hospitals would yield information about a greater number of cases than any other single source. It was fully realised that

> surveillance data on their own will often be insufficient to identify what preventive measures should be taken; for this purpose accidents will often have to be investigated in greater depth at the scene of the accident and as soon after the accident as possible.[2]

The Home Accident Surveillance System (HASS) uses a rolling sample of 20 hospitals in England and Wales offering 24-hour accident and emergency coverage. The total number of home accidents treated at hospitals in England and Wales is about two million a year; another 800 000 accidents in the home each year receive medical treatment from a general practitioner only.

In Scotland about 200 000 cases are treated in hospitals and a further 100 000 by general practitioners. This gives a figure in the order of three million for the overall number of home accidents each year in Great Britain that require some form of medical treatment. The HASS deals with non-fatal accidents.

The HASS data are concerned with products involved in accidents but not responsible for them. From the tables which follow it is apparent that stairs and steps are most frequently involved in home accidents, followed by a person other than the patient, room doors, tins and tin openers, and carpets and underlays. In fatal home accidents stairs and steps lead the general categories, followed by food and drink, smokers' materials, fires and aspirins.

Detailed studies have been carried out on a number of products including electric hedgetrimmers, electric drills, powered saws, liquified petroleum gas, vehicle maintenance, bouncing cradles, inhalation hazards and electric blankets.

Associated methodological studies include a survey of the effects of home accidents on the lives of patients and their families and the demands on the medical resources of hospitals and general practitioners. The aim is to provide a database for a priority model for use by the Department of Trade and Industry when making cost-benefit analyses of proposals for legislation and other measures to improve consumer safety.

The Home Accident Deaths Database (HADD) is a database for fatal home accidents compatible with that provided by the HASS for non-fatal cases. It combines records converted from the computerised data of the Office of Population, Censuses and Surveys (OPCS) and the Home Office (on deaths in fires) with manually encoded records from death registration forms from OPCS and electrical fatality report forms from the Area Electricity Boards.

The database is, therefore, neither as homogeneous nor, in some respects, as detailed as the HASS data but it is more product orientated and more easily interrogated than the existing sources of information on fatal home accidents. Regular recording began with data for 1982 and in the following year 4599 deaths were listed.

In November 1986 Mr Michael Howard, the Minister for Corporate and Consumer Affairs, announced a new source of information to help prevent accidents. It is a new computer-based information system on hazardous products set up with the co-operation of the enforcement authorities to complement the HASS. The new system will be built on the foundation of the computerised system of information established by the Institute of Trading Standards Administration, known as TS-Link. The essential inputs will be reports about potentially hazardous consumer products which have probably not so far caused injury, but which have given cause for concern.

# FATAL HOME ACCIDENTS

## Table 2 *General categories of products, articles and features of the home involved in the accidents*

| General Category | Number of accidents | General Category | Number of accidents |
|---|---|---|---|
| Baby and child furniture | 9 | Smoking implements and sources of ignition (including fuels and gases) | 360 |
| Baby and child transport | 1 | Kitchen utensils | 3 |
| Cleaning equipment | 0 | Laundry equipment | 4 |
| Cleaning products | 7 | Leisure/hobbies equipment – adults | 0 |
| Clothing and clothing accessories | 87 | Lighting equipment | 27 |
| Stereo, radio and telephone equipment | 12 | Luggage/personal carrying equipment | 0 |
| Constructional features of the house | 719 | Medicinal products | 334 |
| Containers and wrappings | 23 | Miscellaneous household equipment | 10 |
| Cooking appliances | 45 | Feature of outside environment (other than plants and trees) | 63 |
| Do-it-yourself tools and equipment | 103 | Personal items and personal hygiene | 26 |
| Dust/dirt/wood particles | 1 | Pets' articles | 1 |
| Electrical wiring and accessories | 80 | Plants and trees | 6 |
| Flammable/corrosive liquids (other than domestic bleach) | 10 | Playthings and sports equipment | 24 |
| Food and drink (other than hot liquids) | 394 | Sewing and knitting equipment | 2 |
| Footwear | 1 | Stationery, writing and drawing equipment | 2 |
| Freezing/refrigerator equipment | 0 | Vehicles (other than baby's transport) | 59 |
| Garden equipment and tools | 14 | Walking aids | 2 |
| Imprecisely specified articles | 11 | Wall and floor furnishings and coverings | 0 |
| Heating and ventilation equipment | 254 | Waste disposal | 0 |
| Household fixtures | 84 | Pets/insects | 2 |
| Household furnishings | 26 | | |
| Household furniture | 224 | | |
| Household linen | 126 | No article specified | 2276 |
| Hot liquids and vapours | 70 | | |
| | | Total for table | 5502 |
| | | Total for accidents | 4592 |

*Notes*

1 As either one or two articles (or none) can be recorded for each accident, the total number is different from the total number of accidents. An average of 0.7 articles per accident was recorded, because for some types of accident (eg falls on the level) little or no information is available on any products involved.

2 'Involved' does not necessarily imply cause or fault.

*Source: The Home Accident Surveillance System. Report of the 1985 Data* (1986) Department of Trade and Industry.

# FATAL HOME ACCIDENTS

## Table 3 *Products, articles and features of the home most frequently involved in the accidents*

| Category | Number of accidents | Category | Number of accidents |
|---|---|---|---|
| Stairs/steps | 587 | Car | 29 |
| Food and drink | 296 | Electric blanket | 25 |
| Smokers' materials | 168 | Boiler/water heater | 25 |
| Fire (controlled heat) | 150 | Cold water | 23 |
| Asprin/painkiller | 116 | Caravan | 21 |
| Carbon monoxide | 110 | Roof | 19 |
| Blanket/sheet/bedspread | 109 | Polythene bag | 18 |
| Specified medicinal product | 104 | Floors, unspecified covering | 16 |
| Sleeping pills etc | 98 | String/rope | 16 |
| Household furniture | 91 | Pond/stream/river | 16 |
| Clothing | 87 | Material – cloth etc | 15 |
| Wiring/plug/socket | 80 | Unspecified medicinal product | 14 |
| Bed | 72 | Candle | 13 |
| Bath and fittings | 71 | Balcony | 12 |
| Alcohol | 70 | Specified heating/ventilating equipment | 12 |
| Window | 65 | Carpet/underlay | 12 |
| Hot water in bath | 61 | Television | 11 |
| Ladder/stepladder | 52 | Rubbish | 11 |
| Matches | 47 | Other person | 11 |
| Cooker | 44 | Swimming/paddling pool | 11 |
| Chair | 40 | Solvent | 10 |
| Space heater | 31 | Lamp (any kind) | 10 |

*Notes*

1 Only those categories with a frequency of 10 or more have been presented.

2 'Involved' does not necessarily imply cause or fault.

3 As either one or two articles (or none) can be recorded for each accident, the total number is different from the total number of accidents. An average of 0.7 articles per accident was recorded, because for some types of accident (eg falls on the level) little or no information is available on any products involved.

*Source: The Home Accident Surveillance System. Report of the 1985 Data* (1986) Department of Trade and Industry.

## NON-FATAL HOME ACCIDENTS

### Table 4 *Products, articles and features of the home most frequently involved in the accidents*

| Category | Number of accidents | Category | Number of accidents |
|---|---|---|---|
| Stairs/steps | 10149 | Pieces/planks of wood | 1140 |
| Person (other than patient) | 7382 | Hot water | 1128 |
| Doors (to rooms) | 4366 | Cars/parts | 1127 |
| Tins/tin openers | 3000 | Non-domestic knives | 1102 |
| Carpet/underlay | 2646 | Doors (unspecified) | 1091 |
| Chairs | 2646 | Splinters | 1061 |
| Beds/bunk beds | 2554 | Sofas/couches | 971 |
| Floors | 2277 | Hot drinks | 932 |
| Footwear | 2154 | Terraces/outside yards | 899 |
| Tables/coffee tables | 1916 | Bare feet/socks | 853 |
| Ladders/step ladders | 1534 | Knives (unspecified) | 850 |
| Nails/screws/tacks | 1499 | Pills/tablets | 821 |
| Windows | 1490 | Bottles (glass and plastic) | 821 |
| Glass (unspecified) | 1481 | Dogs | 787 |
| Walls | 1449 | Stools/pouffes | 764 |
| Cupboards/cabinets | 1262 | Walls (outside) | 754 |
| Paths | 1199 | Baths and fittings | 752 |
| Toys | 1183 | Bones | 718 |
| Domestic knives | 1147 | Carving knives/carvers | 715 |

*Notes*

1  Only those categories with a frequency of 700 or more have been presented.

2  'Involved' does not necessarily imply cause or fault.

3  As either one or two articles (or none) can be recorded for each accident, the total number is different from the total number of accidents. An average of 1.3 articles per accident was reported.

*Source: The Home Accident Surveillance System. Report of the 1985 Data* (1986) Department of Trade and Industry.

The sources of information will include:

— Direct consumer complaints either to local authorities or to the Consumer Safety Unit of the Department of Trade and Industry.

— Voluntary recalls of products by manufacturers.

— Warnings to the public about potentially unsafe products, issued either by Central Government, local authorities or by suppliers themselves.

— Results of laboratory tests of suspect products.

— Reports from enforcement authorities about potentially unsafe goods found in the market.

Mr Howard said that

Apart from such obvious information as numbers, dates and sources of complaints, it will tell us about brand names and trade marks, identity marks or features, countries of origin, names of manufacturers or importers, the nature of the hazard, the result of any tests and what action was taken as a result of the complaint in each case. In our development work we should constantly bear in mind the potential for linking our system with other national and international sources of information about hazardous consumer products, including those, operating within the Community and in OECD.

## UNITED STATES

An original pilot scheme was based on a sample of 119 hospitals drawn in 1970 and was fully operational by 1972. Over the years this has been refined and a new sample of 73 hospitals has emerged with 250 000 cases annually. Computer terminals at each hospital are on-line with the central computer of the Consumer Products Safety Commission, near Washington, and reports are sent in daily. The National Electronic Injury Surveillance System (NEISS) allows both routine surveillance and more in-depth follow up as required. It is said to be the most important epidemiological tool available to the Consumer Product Safety Commission. At the surveillance level NEISS provides information on who is being injured, by what products and the nature of the injury.

## THE NETHERLANDS

A pilot study was carried out in four hospitals in 1981 and 1982 and the system was set up in 1983 to record all accidents that fall outside the category of road and industrial accidents. The scheme is called Prive Ongevallen Registratie Systeem (PORS) and uses a rolling sample of 14 hospitals. The league table of products involved in accidents is led by bicycles followed by step ladders, doors and mopeds.

## NORDIC COUNTRIES

The Nordic Steering Committee for Product Safety started a pilot project in 1976 in Sweden to test a method of collecting data on accidents. In 1979 the Nordic Council of Ministers recommended that recording systems should be developed to give an overall picture of accidents and injuries.

**Denmark.** In Odense, Arhus and Randers research projects for recording accidents have been carried out for several years. The Danish Board for Health and Social Welfare has proposed a scheme for the continuous recording of accidents at all hospitals.

**Norway.** Several research projects have laid the foundation for a project at the National Institute of Public Health for the establishment of a nation-wide register of illness and injury.

**Finland.** A number of research projects have been carried out but the Finnish accident registration projects are mainly to be found in Helsinki.

**Iceland.** Registration of accidents has been going on continuously at the Borgarspital in Reykjavik since 1968.

**Sweden.** A number of research projects have been carried out but the National Swedish Board for Consumer Policies considers that the lack of any overall system for the reporting of accidents in the home and during leisure time, and the maintenance of their statistics, is a fundamental shortcoming in Sweden's present system of consumer protection.

## EEC

In 1977 the European Commission convened a group of experts from the Member States to look into the implementation of a data collection system on accidents in the home involving the use of certain products. A pilot experiment started in January 1982 with national authorities meeting regularly to examine problems connected with data collection and transmission. Data were collected in hospital casualty departments in Belgium, Denmark, France, Ireland, Italy, The Netherlands and the United Kingdom.

After 30 months the pilot study enabled the Commission to submit to the Council of Ministers a proposal for a Community system which would cover home accidents, and in addition sports and leisure activities.

The European Commission has estimated that the number of victims of accidents in which consumer products are involved is as high as 30 000 dead (8000 of them children) and 40 million injured each year.

## INFORMATION EXCHANGE SCHEMES

1    **The Community Rapid Information Exchange.** An informal information exchange system on the safety of foodstuffs was set up in 1978; about one case of dangerous foodstuffs per month is reported to the Commission network. The following year the Commission submitted to the Council of Ministers a proposal for a system for the rapid exchange of information on the dangers arising from the use of consumer goods, so that responsible authorities could take the necessary measures promptly to ensure public safety.

Four years later the proposal was accepted for an experimental period, which will end in 1988. Three elements of information are required from a Member State: the means of identification of the product concerned, the nature and gravity of the risks and the steps which the Member State has decided to take. These elements are verified by the Commission which then sends the information to all other Member States. Feedback from the actions taken enables an appraisal to be made of their efficiency and effect in dealing with the particular danger reported.

2    **European Bureau of Consumers' Unions** (Bureau Européen des Unions de Consommateurs — BEUC). This organisa-

tion has correspondents in 15 European countries and its information exchange covers all consumer products in the widest sense. On average it deals with 1.5 notifications a month.

3    **International Organisation of Consumers' Unions** (IOCU). There are correspondents in 34 countries and offices in Brussels and Penang. IOCU comprises 120 member organisations in 50 countries and it exchanges information with BEUC. On average it deals with 1.5 notifications of dangerous products each month through its information exchange system.

## SUMMARY

There is a surprising lack of information with regard to which products are responsible for accidents. In the United Kingdom and the United States there are well-established systems which record information on which products are *involved* in home accidents and provide raw data for regulatory and legislative bodies. The EEC and consumer organisations operate information exchange schemes on dangerous consumer products.

## REFERENCES

1    *Report of the Royal Commission on Civil Liability and Compensation for Personal Injury.* Cmnd 7054-I. London, HMSO, March 1978.
2    *Collection of Information on Accidents in the Home* (1976) Department of Prices and Consumer Protection. London, HMSO.

# CHAPTER 7

# IDENTIFICATION OF RISKS 2
Hazard Analysis and Risk Assessment

## INTRODUCTION

People are exposed to a variety of hazards in every aspect of life: physical from the forces of nature and human activity; chemical from acute and chronic poisons; biological from infectious organisms; and psychological from social relationships. The most dramatic and most easily recognised of these are the physical hazards, because of the immediate and obvious relationship between cause and effect.

Public interest in and concern with hazards have grown, as the media have brought into every home pictures of the latest disaster and the efforts of the community to cope with it. But the views of the physicists, the chemists, the biologists and the psychologists are by no means identical. Indeed, the statisticians, epidemiologists, doctors and economists can each add another dimension to the differences. In 1983 the Royal Society in the UK published a survey of risk assessment which is probably the first attempt to cover the many different disciplines involved. Those interested in obtaining a pragmatic introduction to risk reduction should read the report.[1] It will help to put the subject into perspective and explain why there can be no single answer.

This chapter, which reviews some of the hazard analysis and risk assessment techniques, must be seen as but a brief examination of some of the ways in which hazards can be identified and the risks they present evaluated.

Hazard analysis is a sophisticated technique for good organisations who wish to allocate their resources sensibly and improve their standards. It should not be used until the basic management is satisfactory. If (management) do not run a 'tight ship', if the people are not trained, if there are no instructions, if no one cares or monitors, then the error rates will be much higher and hazard analysis a waste of time. First improve the management. Is the result of the hazard analysis in accordance with experience and common sense? If not, the hazard analysis must be wrong.[2]

## HAZARD OR RISK

First, we have to establish that 'hazard' and 'risk' are not synonyms, even if the *Oxford English Dictionary* thinks that they are

Hazard — a set of conditions in the operation of a product or system with the potential for initiating an accident sequence (BS 4778 13.3.1) a potential source of harm.

Risk   — the combined effect of the probability of occurrence of an undesirable event, and the magnitude of that event (BS 4778 13.3.2) a·measure of the probability and severity of harm.

If we look at hazards by themselves we have no way of knowing what threat they present. We will not know what the chances are of the threat becoming a reality, or how serious the outcome would be. A probabilistic approach will see a hazard in terms of the risk of failure and its consequences. This has the advantage of enabling the decision as to acceptability to be externalised from the design process and examined in a logical manner.

The identification of hazards is dependent on the knowledge, experience and imagination of the analyst. Check-lists of hazards are not an alternative to thinking, but should be regarded more as *aides-mémoire*. Each analyst should develop a list which concentrates on his company's own products. A very open mind is necessary, with a facility for lateral thinking being a considerable advantage. One may well dismiss 'flying objects' from the hazards that could be presented by a television set, but one television repair man had the sight of one eye damaged by a spring-loaded control which flew off a set he was servicing and hit him in the face.

In risk assessment subjective values can be based on a simple scoring system and the judgement of the analyst. There are also data banks which have been developed within various industries and cover a wide range of components, systems and instruments. These data banks provide statistically based measures of reliability derived from a large number of actual instances. Their use needs care because of the great variety of practice in categorisation and allocation, and the proprietary nature of much of the material.

Remember that hazard analysis and risk assessment techniques are aids to management. They are not a substitute for the pragmatic engineer or scientist.

Two of the chief techniques can be characterised as the top-down method and bottom-up method. In the first an adverse event is the starting point and the analyst works towards discovering what failures could cause it to happen. In the second the individual components or sub-systems are examined and the consequences of a failure or a series of failures developed. The first method is Fault Tree Analysis and the second is Failure Mode and Effect Analysis.

## FAULT TREE ANALYSIS (FTA)

This technique was used by NASA in the space programmes of the 1960s and 1970s, having been developed by Bell Telephone in 1961. The nuclear industry has seen the greatest use of FTA. It is a convenient way of representing the logical connection between the failure modes of a system. The top of the tree, the top event, can be evaluated both qualitatively and quantitatively, with the aid of a computer where appropriate. FTA is defined as:

> The study of the possible sequence of events constituting the failure of a system using the diagrammatic method of algorithms. (BS 4778 17.9)

The first step is to define the system that is to be analysed, to prevent the tree from becoming too complex. A tree can only analyse one top event and so a number may be needed for one product. A system can be divided into its operation phases in order that each can be analysed separately, such as start-up, run, and shut-down.

The next step is the selection of the top event, which is the undesirable event, such as a fire, explosion or the failure of a system, sub-system or assembly. The tree then develops by the

Figure 1 *Some basic Fault Tree symbols*

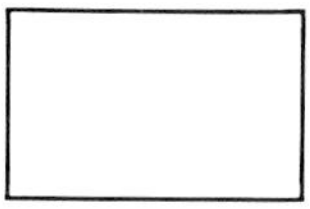

An event, usually a fault, resulting from
the combination of more basic faults.

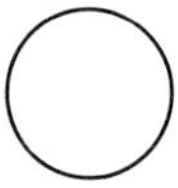

Basic component fault which can be assigned
a probability of occurrence based on test results
or physics of failure analysis.

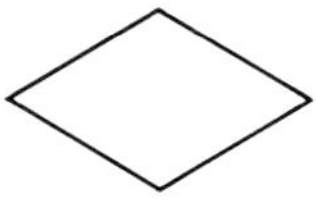

A fault not developed further as to its causes
because of lack of information, time,
or value in doing so.

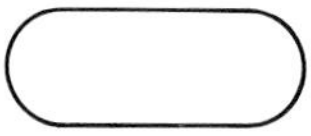

A conditional event – one which must occur
in order for an input fault (cause) to
result in an output fault (effect).

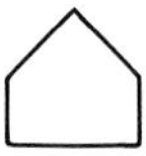

An event expected to occur in
normal operation.

AND gate – the output event occurs only
when all of the input events are present.

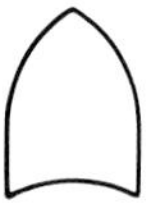

OR gate – the output event occurs when
one or more of the input events are present.

Reference key to another part of the
fault tree where the identical sequence
of events is shown.

identification of the logical combination of the failure modes that would result in the occurrence of the top event.

The modes of failure can have a variety of causes, such as the breakdown of an individual component, operator error, the failure of a test procedure or a maintenance programme. The failure modes are combined in a number of ways which are called gates. The most common are the OR gate and the AND gate, which represent a particular condition or failed state within the system. An OR gate will satisfy the logic if any one failure mode connected to the gate exists.

For an AND gate all the failure modes feeding into the gate must exist to satisfy the logic. There are other types of gate that can be used, some of which have specialised applications.

Basic fault tree symbols are shown in Figure 1. A rectangle is used to represent an output event caused by the inputs from the level below; it is at the same time an input to the level above. A circle is a basic fault event, such as a component failure or a human error, and ends its particular branch of the tree because it has no output. A diamond symbolises a secondary factor which could lead to the primary failure. A house represents an event that always occurs.

The analyst identifies the events on the next level down that could cause the top event, and determines whether they will happen as an AND function or an OR function. He continues to develop the tree in this manner, using the symbols, until the lowest possible level is reached and the basic failure event identified. Having completed the tree the analyst will now evaluate it to discover what specific actions are required and make the appropriate recommendations. Figure 2 is an example of a simple fault tree.

The construction of the fault tree should follow a methodical procedure by first identifying general events, ie failure states, which when logically combined will result in the undesired top event. These events can be considered as the second level of the fault tree. Each event on this second level should be developed in the same methodical manner until all of the basic failure modes of the analysis have been included. These failure modes are often referred to as components of the fault tree. Computer codes exist which will convert network diagrams into fault trees.

A useful means of identifying the failure modes which should be included in the fault tree is through a Failure Modes and Effect Analysis (FMEA), see below. Although an FMEA

Figure 2 *Simple Fault Tree Analysis: mains-operated electric food mixer*

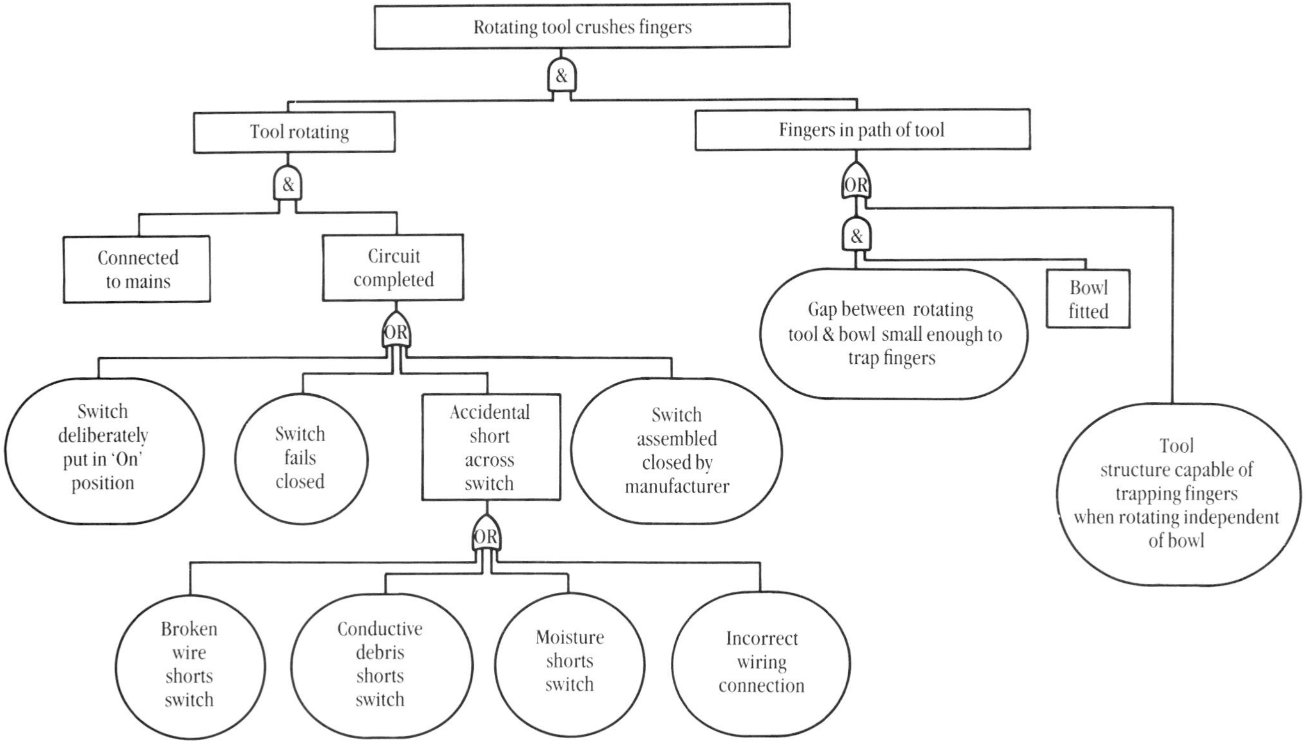

*Source:* Boswell, D and Brewer, R 'Guide to the management of product safety and occupational health and safety.' Draft BSI publication.

does not in itself establish the logical connection between failure modes, it is a process which traces the effects of a failure and as such it is a useful tool in the construction of the fault tree, particularly where the same component failure appears in more than one branch of the tree.[3] (See Case History 1.)

## FAILURE MODE AND EFFECT ANALYSIS (FMEA)

The mental discipline that a designer should go through during the design process is reflected in an FMEA. It aims at anticipating potential failures so that their source can be eliminated. It is basic hazard analysis which was originally developed from reliability estimating procedures, to which risk considerations have been added. FMEA is defined as:

> The study of the potential failures that might occur in any part of a system to determine the probable effect of each on all the other parts of the system and on probable operational success (BS 4778 17.7).

To be correct we should distinguish between FMEA and FMECA, that is Failure Mode Effect and Criticality Analysis, which is defined as:

> The study of the potential failures that might occur in any part of a system to determine the probable effect of each on all the other parts of the system and on probable operational success, the results of which are ranked in order of seriousness (BS 4778 17.8).

The difference between FMEA and FMECA lies in the ranking of the results, which is part of the latter exercise but not the former. However, we will follow common practice and use FMEA to cover both techniques.

Many companies use FMEA, although probably less than the number who claim to use it. The pioneers were in the defence, aerospace, automotive and nuclear industries. Today companies in such industries use FMEA as part of the contractual requirements they insist on their suppliers fulfilling. Often a procedure document will lay down how the FMEA should be performed, who should be part of the evaluation team, the method of results presentation and how corrective action is to be effected.

An FMEA is not an addition to an engineer's workload but a disciplined technique that enables him to perform his job more effectively. A good FMEA is one which:

— identifies known and potential failure modes

— identifies the causes and effects of each failure mode

— gives each identified failure mode a priority number according to the probability and severity of its risk and the chance of detection before failure occurs, and

— provides for corrective action.

Special forms and ranking tables are used to carry out an FMEA. A simple example is given in Tables 5 and 6 and the key elements of the information it contains are described below.

**Failure mode.** The analyst has to anticipate how the part being considered could fail. It is not a question of whether it *will* fail but rather how it *could* fail. Consider a tie bar bracket which is part of a vehicle engine mounting system which stabilises all movement of the engine. The bracket could have a number of failure modes, eg bracket fractures, bracket corrodes, fixing bolts loosen, fixing bolts fracture, bracket bends and so on. These are all listed and each possibility is then analysed under the following headings.

**Effect of failure.** The result of the first failure mode, of the bracket fracturing, would be the removal of its stabilising function and the transfer of all motion of the engine to its mountings. The same effect would be produced by the other failure modes, but the cause would not necessarily be the same in each case.

**Cause of failure.** The analyst has to anticipate what could cause the failure mode to occur and describe the conditions that bring it about. In the example the brackets could fracture because of an inadequate specification of hole to edge distance for the fixing bolts. The cause of the bracket corroding could be the inadequate specification for the preparation of the bracket, such as the type of coating.

**Occurrence of failure.** The analyst must now use his knowledge and experience to estimate the probability of the bracket actually failing. He has to assess the likelihood of occurrence using an evaluation scale of 1 to 10, with 1 indicating a very low probability of occurrence and 10 indicating a near certainty of occurrence. The score for the first failure mode in the example is given as 1: very low probability of occurrence, theoretically possible only.

**Severity of failure.** The question here is: what is the consequence of failure? How severe will it be? The same evaluation scale is used, with 1 indicating a minor nuisance and 10 a very serious consequence. The score in the example is given as 7: failure causes total loss of engine mounting stabilisation. Further use could cause eventual safety-critical failure.

**Detection of failure.** The analyst has to estimate the chance of a potential failure being detected before the end-user finds it. The evaluation scale is still 1 to 10 but the weighting is reversed: with 1 indicating a very high probability that failure would be detected before it reached the end-user, and 10 showing a very low probability of detection. The score in the example is given as 10: almost impossible to detect before item reaches customer.

**Risk priority number.** This is the product of the estimates of occurrence, severity and detection and provides a relative priority of the failure mode. The higher the number the more serious is the failure mode. The list of risk priority numbers will highlight the top priority areas for action. The risk priority number for the failure of the bracket caused by inadequate hole specification is $1 \times 7 \times 10 = 70$.

**Corrective action.** The follow-up is critical to the use of an FMEA. The analyst must provide sound corrective actions to deal with the potential failure modes that have been identified in the analysis.

The above example is a simple explanation of an FMEA but more sophisticated variations are used, some developed to meet the requirements of particular products. Fault Tree Analysis (see page 59) can provide a filter with which to discover the most critical failure modes before applying FMEA. The classification of failure frequency is at the heart of FMEA and the most reliable information will come from the data banks. Care is needed to establish that the particular application and life cycle under analysis are compatible with the data bank failure rate. A simple classification system can be used for a first pass to isolate the more critical areas for more detailed analysis.

Severity scales can be developed to fit the product line of the company. The extremes of a scale are usually fairly easy to

# FAILURE MODE & EFFECT ANALYSIS
Table 5 *Part of vehicle engine mounting system*

| Component | Failure mode | Effect of failure | Cause of failure | 1 | 2 | 3 | 4 | Corrective action |
|---|---|---|---|---|---|---|---|---|
| Tie bar bracket | Bracket fractures | Stabilising function of tie bar removed. All motion of engine transferred to mountings | Inadequate specification of hole to edge distance | 1 | 7 | 10 | 70 | Test suitability of specification |
| | Bracket corrodes | As above | Inadequate specification for preparation of tie bracket | 1 | 5 | 10 | 50 | Test suitability of specification |
| | Fixing bolts loosen | As above | Bolt torque inadequately specified | 5 | 5 | 8 | 200 | Test for loosening |
| | | | Bolt material or thread type inadequate | 1 | 5 | 10 | 50 | Test suitability of specification |

*Notes*

1 Occurrence
*Score*
1 very low probability
10 near certainty

2 Severity
1 minor nuisance

3 Chance of detection
*Score*
1 very high probability
10 very low probability

4 Risk priority
$1 \times 2 \times 3$

| Component | Failure mode | Effect of failure | Cause of failure | 1 | 2 | 3 | 4 | Corrective action |
|---|---|---|---|---|---|---|---|---|
| Tie bar bracket (continued) | Fixing bolts fracture | As above | Bolts incorrectly specified | 4 | 7 | 10 | 280 | Test bolts for fracture |
| | | | Bolt torque specification too high | 5 | 7 | 8 | 280 | Test suitability of torque specification |
| | Bracket bends | As above | Material thickness inadequately specified | 1 | 5 | 10 | 50 | Test suitability of specification |
| | | | No flexibility in bracket to the bar when rotational loads applied | 7 | 5 | 10 | 350 | Redesign bush to allow for flexibility under rotational loads |

*Notes*

*1 Occurrence*

*Score*
1 very low probability
10 near certainty

*2 Severity*
1 minor nuisance
10 serious safety hazard

*3 Chance of detection*

*Score*
1 very high probability
2 very low probability

*4 Risk priority number*
$1 \times 2 \times 3$

## FAILURE MODE AND EFFECT ANALYSIS RANKING TABLE

Table 6 *Tie bar bracket, part of vehicle engine mounting system, stabilises all movement of engine*

| Rating | Occurrence | Severity | Detection |
|---|---|---|---|
| 1 | Very low probability of occurrence theoretically possible only | Visual non-functional failure only. Hardly noticeable | Almost certain to be detected during test or inspection before item reaches user |
| 2 | Low probability of occurrence during design life | | Very likely to be detected |
| 3 | | | Likely to be detected |
| 4 | | | |
| 5 | Moderate | Failure causes reduction in engine mounting stabilisation and requires attention | Could be detected |
| 6 | | | |
| 7 | | Failure causes total loss of engine mounting stabilisation. Further use could cause eventual safety critical failure of engine mountings | |
| 8 | High | | Unlikely to be detected |
| 9 | | Vehicle unusable but not safety critical | Very unlikely to be detected before item reaches customer |
| 10 | Very high probability of occurrence. Very likely to occur during design life | Safety-critical failure. Vehicle off road after catastrophic failure | Almost impossible to detect before item reaches customer |

determine but the levels in between may require much consideration. If a scale of commercial damage is measured in money for the purposes of graduation, the severity of the loss of £1 million will depend on the financial viability of the company. A multinational would scarcely notice such a sum but it could spell disaster for a small company.

The threshold of ruin is unique to each company. The severity of an injury can be measured in a number of ways, such as cost, time off work or the assignment of a medical value; the UK Home Accident Surveillance System and the US National Electronic Injury Surveillance System use different methods for measuring severity, see Chapter 6.

There is another factor that can be taken into account, the degree of imperilment can be classified where appropriate. The concept is concerned with the spontaneity of failure. Some failures are progressive and give plenty of warning that they are going to happen, so that their effect is limited. Other failures occur instantaneously and produce a catastrophe without any warning at all. Yet other failures present no hazard whether they occur slowly or spontaneously. One ranking of imperilment has four levels:

— Rapid or spontaneous. No effect.

— Warning sufficient for the prudent.

— Warning for skilled who can avoid injury.

— Instantaneous. No evasive action possible.[4]

The preparation of an FMEA for each possible failure mode can be a lengthy process. It may present some ideas that are unusual to many engineers. Its aim is to show in a logical form the consequences of failure so that corrective action can be taken. It can open a previously undiscovered window to allow a new perspective to be obtained on product safety.

## THE SAFETY PROFILE

The technique was originally intended for small components, but it can be extended for application to equipment. The basis is a grid with ordinates of probability and criticality.

To prepare a product safety profile all potential injury-producing failure modes, their cause and their effect are identified. For each mode, or event, two factors are established: the probability and the hazard index. These are put together graphically to provide the safety profile of the product. The more complete the input data the more accurate will be the profile, although this may mean testing to failure rather than the usual tendency to test for conformance to specification. The first step is to define all possible failures that could cause a safety hazard, and here an FMEA is valuable. The effect of each potential failure mode is ranked for probability and hazard; where statistical data are not available an estimate is made using, for instance, 1, 2, 3, 4 and 5 as ranking levels for very low, low, medium, high and very high.

For each failure mode the hazard index is entered on the grid along the x axis and the probability of failure is plotted on the y axis. The most serious failure modes will gather in the upper right-hand corner of the matrix and the least serious in the lower left-hand corner.

The size and shape of the profile demonstrates the degree of safety of the component or product under analysis. There are a number of variations that can be used in the construction of a safety profile; such as the inclusion of a hazard index as a function of time so that the hazard increases as the time available to avoid injury decreases. Figure 3 shows a simple example of a product safety profile.

## DELPHI TECHNIQUE

In Greek mythology the earth was flat and circular, with Greece occupying the middle and Delphi at its centre. The great temple of Apollo in Delphi housed a sacred stone, which was believed to mark the actual centre of the world.

There were many oracles in Greece, but the Delphi oracle was the most famous. It exercised supreme control, and the phenomenal expansion of Greece was inspired and directed largely by its priestess, who pronounced her cryptic revelations or counsels. The members of elite Delphi families sat around a tripod occupied by the priestess and transmitted her utterances to posterity. This interpretation was necessary because a Delphi utterance was one which had ambiguity associated with it.

Today, in business, decision making under conditions of uncertainty is often based on a group judgement. The board will

Figure 3 *Product safety profile: mains-operated TV receiver*

| Hazard letter | Hazards | Product life phase risk rankings | | | | | | | | | Product |
|---|---|---|---|---|---|---|---|---|---|---|---|
| | | Acceptance testing | Transport | Storage | Installation | Normal operation | Misuse/Failure | Maintenance | Disposal | Other | Notes: Key to Rank No's. Rank No's 2/5 indicate occurrence risk 2 and criticality risk 5. Worst combination is underlined. *Causes & Comments* |
| A | Electric shock | 2/5 | - | - | 2/5 | 1/5 | 3/5 | 2/5 | - | - | With rear cover off |
| B | Fire | 1/2 | 1/2 | 1/5 | 1/2 | 1/5 | 2/5 | 1/2 | 1/5 | - | Organic materials in cabinet & components |
| C | Explosion | 1/4 | 2/4 | - | 1/4 | 1/3 | 1/4 | 1/4 | 2/4 | - | Damage to CRT |
| D | Toxic fumes | 1/2 | - | - | 1/2 | 1/3 | 1/3 | 1/3 | 3/3 | - | Overheating or burning of organic materials |
| E | Radiation | - | - | - | - | - | 1/2 | - | - | - | Not normally hazardous |
| F | Harmful substances | - | - | - | - | - | - | - | 1/3 | - | Contamination of environment due to careless disposal |
| G | Cutting/ crushing | 1/2 | 3/3 | - | 3/2 | - | - | 2/3 | 2/3 | - | Handling into position |
| H | Surface temperature | 1/2 | - | - | 1/2 | 1/3 | 1/3 | 1/3 | - | - | With rear cover off |
| I | Psychological | - | - | - | - | 5/5 | - | - | - | - | Harmful programmes, eg incitement to violence |

*Analysis date*

*Recommended actions:*
  i) Hazard warnings for letters A, B, C, D, F, G, H.
  ii) All organic materials to have Oxygen Index greater than 27.
  iii) Fit cut-outs activated by smoke-detector, overload current, excess temperature.
  iv) MD to receive and initial a copy of this Safety Profile.

Harm occurrence — Higher risk

| Harm occurrence | 1 | 2 | 3 | 4 | 5 |
|---|---|---|---|---|---|
| 5 | | | | | I |
| 4 | | | | | |
| 3 | | | DG | | A |
| 2 | | E | | C | B |
| 1 | | | FH | | |

Lower risk — Harm criticality

Source: Boswell, D and Brewer, R 'Guide to the Management of Product Safety and Occupational Health and Safety'. Draft BSI publication.

have to reach agreement on critical questions for which inadequate information is available. The most common way of obtaining these group judgements is by the members sitting around the same table and reaching a consensus by face-to-face interactions. This has the disadvantages of conflicting schedules, time constraints, geographical separation, dominance by individuals, irrelevant communication and the group pressure for conformity.

To overcome these disadvantages the Delphi Technique was developed by the Rand Corporation in the United States to enable geographically dispersed warfare experts to forecast military developments. Because of its confidential application, it remained a classified technique until the 1960s. Since then its use has spread with organisations adopting it for forecasting future events in the United States, Canada, Europe, Japan and the Soviet Union.

The primary objective of Delphi is to determine whether a group of experts, through anonymous and carefully structured interactions, can arrive at consensus about an uncertain state. It is a technique which uses group synthesis in an attempt to reach a decision.[5]

According to one of the Delphi originators two options are available when one is working on a problem under conditions of uncertainty with insufficient data, incomplete decision theory, and a high order of complexity

> we can either wait indefinitely until we have an adequate theory enabling us to deal with sociometric and political problems as confidently as we do with problems in physics and chemistry, or we can make the most of an admittedly unsatisfactory situation and try to obtain the relevant intuitive insights of experts and then use their judgements as systematically as possible.[6]

The Delphi Technique is a method of eliciting and refining group judgements. The rationale for the procedure is primarily the age-old adage: two heads are better than one where exact knowledge is not available. The procedure has three features:

1    Opinions of members of the group are obtained by formal questionnaire.

2    Interaction is effected by a systematic exercise conducted in several iterations, with carefully controlled feedback between rounds.

3   The group opinion is defined as an appropriate aggregate of individual opinions of the final round.[7]

The disadvantage of the Delphi Technique is that it does not lend itself to all types of decision. A single decision maker can probably make the best decisions in routine matters. The success of the method depends on selecting a suitable panel of experts which can be difficult, and it can take several weeks to complete all the questionnaire rounds in some applications, although the use of data processing equipment can help.

The basic feature of the technique is the filling out of questionnaires by members of the selected group in an anonymous manner; responses can be grouped statistically according to the median score. With repeated measurement the range of response will decrease and converge towards the mid-range of distribution, and the total group response will successively move towards the 'correct' answer.[8]

Feedback and iteration are important in developing the application of the technique, with respondents in the second and subsequent rounds being asked to justify extreme positions. The number of iterations will depend on the degree of group consensus required, but generally they range from one to six. Failure to reach consensus may be as informative as its attainment in some situations.

Published industrial applications of Delphi include forecasts on the market for new and existing products, technological and social events, evaluation of research and development projects, availability and cost of materials, labour and capital, and changes in government attitudes.

There are a number of versions of the Delphi Technique and it is important to use that which most closely matches the problem. For instance, a simplified Delphi method has been used to evaluate the risks presented by hazards associated with product failure. Here it is useful in revealing which exposures are seen to be the most serious facing a company in an area where there are no hard data, or resources are not available to obtain them. With the advent of strict liability in tort, such situations will increase for companies concerned with liability-sensitive products. Where data bank failure rates are available one of the other techniques may be more applicable.

The risks can be scored for each hazard using a one to five scale for probability and severity, with interpretations of each level to give guidance to the degree involved for each score.

| Probability | Score | Severity |
|---|---|---|
| Very high | 5 | Very high |
| *(one in ten)* | | *(£1 000 000)* |
| High | 4 | High |
| Medium | 3 | Medium |
| Low | 2 | Low |
| Very Low | 1 | Very Low |
| *(one in a million)* | | *(£100)* |

In some cases it is sufficient to ask for a probability response, while in others a severity response is a valuable addition. By multiplying the probability by the severity a risk index is obtained, which can help in ranking the different hazards by the degree of risk they present to the company. Such an approach enables the company to tackle the most serious exposures first, always bearing in mind that particular attention should be paid to hazards which have very high probabilities or severities, even though their risk indexes may be low.

The Delphi Technique was used during a Product Safety Audit with the board of a company manufacturing a beverage dispenser. The questions covered a number of areas, but the one of interest is that which dealt with the hazards of electrocution and fire. It was agreed that the electrocution of an employee of a company in which a dispenser was installed was a hazard. Also, there had been occasions on which a dispenser had caught fire (due to a design defect) on a customer's premises, fortunately with comparatively little damage to property and none to people.

Individually, the board members were asked to assess the probability and severity of the risks of electrocution and fire due to a design defect or a manufacturing error. The one to five scoring table shown above was used. A wide range of scores was revealed, with the director responsible for design putting the risk as very low while two of his colleagues put it as high. In the context of a Product Safety Audit, the Delphi proved its value by demonstrating that a risk area had been identified which demanded the board's urgent attention to reach agreement on the degree of exposure that faced the company.

The Delphi Technique can be applied in a very sophisticated manner to obtain a view from a large number of respondents. One organisation which carries out such analyses is (appropriately) Solon[9] which uses advanced computerised and statistical methods. An example is a study of systems and data security where the objective was to identify and rate factors that should be considered by managers with twin responsibilities: integrity for data and private information, and protection and fallback for computer systems and installations and online systems.

A total of 266 factors affecting systems and data security was identified in preliminary research. At the first stage, initial ratings of these factors (in terms of their importance now and in four years' time) were obtained from an international panel of 100 specialists in the field.

At stage two, these ratings were then refined in the context of the consensus views that emerged at stage one. The panel's responses and comments were used as a basis for developing comprehensive checklists. Significant variations between sectors were also noted. From an appraisal of these variations, it was shown how the checklists should be modified and adjusted in different parts of the world and different sectors of activity.

Similar methods have been linked to group discussions and interviewing techniques to add perspective and depth to the information for decision making. The methods have been used successfully in studies of technological markets as well as in studies conducted within large and dispersed organisations.

A word of caution is necessary. The Delphi Technique does not produce scientific or optimal results; it is a heuristic device and as such is a valuable management tool. By itself the technique does not make decisions, but it can aid the decision-making process.

## SUMMARY

A hazard is a potential for harm, while risk is a measure of its probability and severity. There are several hazard analysis and risk assessment techniques which are valuable aids to the management of design risks. Two of the more sophisticated ones are Fault Tree Analysis and Failure Mode and Effect Analysis; the Safety Profile is suitable for small components and the Delphi Technique helps decision making under conditions of uncertainty.

## REFERENCES

**1**    *Risk Assessment* (1983). Report of a Royal Society Study Group, London.

**2**    Kletz, T A (1981) Hazard analysis — the manager and the expert. *Reliability Engineering* 2 (1): pp 35-43.

**3**    Jones, G (1983) Fault tree, or not fault tree, that is the question. *Safety and Reliability* 3 (4).

**4**    Mundel, A B (1975) 'Failure Modes and Effects Analysis as a Means of Product Liability Prevention.' Product Liability Conference, Newark NJ.

**5**    Dunn, M and Hillison, W (1980) The Delphi Technique. *Cost and Management,* pp 32-36.

**6**    Pill, J (1971) The Delphi Method: Substance, Context, A Critique and an Annotated Bibliography. *Socio-Economic Planning Sciences* (5): p 61.

**7**    Dalkey, N C (1969) *The Delphi Method. An Experimental Study of Group Opinion.* The Rand Corporation RM 58-88 PR.

**8**    Taylor, R E (1984) Using the Delphi Method to define marketing problems. *Business.* Oct-Dec: pp 16-22.

**9**    Solon Consultants, 25 Bedford Row, London WC1R 4HE.

# CHAPTER 8

# Risk Reduction Programme for Product Design

There can be no one answer on how to reduce design-related risks. Each company must develop its own strategy within which risk reduction has an important part to play, and how this is done will be very much an individual matter.

This is not the place to detail a model design system, for we are concerned with the management of design for product safety. But, whatever the system, a critical milestone should be the Product Design Specification. It becomes the brief to which the designer will work and sets out the parameters which the final design must achieve. Virtually all functions have a contribution to make and some of the key product safety elements are discussed below.

## PRODUCT DESIGN SPECIFICATION

### The End-user and his Environment

A detailed analysis of who is going to use the product is essential, as this could influence the extent of the safeguards that have to be incorporated. If the end-user has little power of discrimination or awareness of danger the design must accommodate this. A young child, a disabled person or a geriatric will need more protection than a healthy adult. Similarly the picture of the end-user should give indications of foreseeable misuse, which the designer must take into account.

The environment of use is also important. The Product Design Specification should specify where appropriate the optimum and extremes of temperature, humidity, sunlight, vibration, noise, pressure, and so on. The proximity of children or animals may be significant, as may be the periods during which the product may be unattended, whether it is in operation or not.

The information on the end-user and his environment will help answer the question: What are the consequences of failure?

People do stupid things, and that includes the highly intelligent as well as the less bright. Rotary mowers are used to trim hedges, knives to free the slice of bread jammed in the electric toaster, and we have all urged on a tired fire with petrol.

It may be necessary to design a product so that it cannot do certain things in order to ensure the safety of the end-user, thus designing for product safety can be both positive and negative. In defining the end-user and his environment a method of including some creative thinking may be helpful. For example, consideration of the following checklist of human hazards may repay study and investigation as they may occur in connection with the products that designers design.

| | |
|---|---|
| Ignorance | Physical skills |
| Overqualification | Horseplay |
| Boredom | Improper or insufficient training |
| Loafing | Alcohol |
| Daydreaming | Drugs |
| Negligence | Physical limitation |
| Carelessness | Sickness |
| Indifference | Exhaustion |
| Supervisory direction | Emotional distress |
| Overproduction | Disorientation |
| Poor judgement | Personal conflicts |
| Short cuts | Vandalism |

The manner and the circumstances of use can be approached in a similar way. The following modes of product usage show some of the ways in which the product can be treated by the end-user in a variety of situations:

| | |
|---|---|
| Intended operation or use | Industrial use |
| Unintended operation or use | Assembly |
| Expected operation or use | Set-up |
| Misuse | Installation |
| Emergency use | Certification |
| Abuse | Testing |
| Inspection | Storage |
| Maintenance | Shipping |
| Service | Modification |
| Repair | Starting, stopping |

| | |
|---|---|
| Cleaning | Changing modes of operation |
| Packaging | Isolation |
| Recreational use | Disposal |
| Commercial use | Salvaging |

## Promotional Material

If a company wishes to make specific claims for the product regarding safety in, say, performance this should be made known right at the outset. In this way the Product Design Specification can be developed to accommodate the claim as an integral part of the process. If the public were led to believe that a product was especially safe, because of its advertising and promotional material, it could be disastrous if a user were injured because of a design defect. (See Case History 15.)

Some products are dangerous by their nature — a chain-saw for instance — but the benefits to society outweigh the risks, providing that the latter are clearly made known to the end-user. With such products the provision of warnings can become critical to the overall safety of the product, and these sensitive areas should be identified in advance and included in the Product Design Specification.

## Standards and Codes of Practice

All relevant standards, codes of practice and customarily accepted practices of a particular industry must be met. But these are minimal from a design point of view and should be thought of as floors and not ceilings. The standards of other countries should be examined, even if the product will not be sold abroad. It is always an advantage to be able to influence the course of events and representation on the standard-making body could be helpful in forecasting future trends.

Many standards are concerned with performance and measurement and have nothing to do with safety at all. The Product Design Specification should include a review of relevant standards, but it should not be assumed that compliance will result in a safe product.

## Legal Requirements

There are two sources of legally required standards: UK

legislation and EEC Directives. Unlike many standards and codes of practice these have to be followed. Sometimes UK legislation will adopt a British Standard and make it mandatory. For instance, no crash-helmet can be sold in the UK unless it conforms to the relevant British Standard. A Secretary of State can make regulations concerning specific products, and in some cases British Standards have been used. In a similar way EEC Directives are increasingly adopting mandatory standards.

A legal requirement can come about in a different way. If a product is being designed for a customer the contract may say that certain standards must be met. The contract may incorporate a specification for the product and here product safety criteria will need to be examined with care.

Expressions such as 'presents no danger to the user' or 'safe for use in the home' have no finite meaning (see Chapter 5). It may be necessary to define the level of safety required and include this in the Product Design Specification.

## Litigation Information

A review of relevant cases concerning the product and personal injury or damage can be rewarding when the final design is being developed. Here will be specific information on what has gone wrong in the past and whether a defect was attributable to a failure in design, manufacture or warnings. By far the majority of design defect claims are settled out of court, which means that case law is merely the tip of the iceberg. (See Case Histories 13, 14, 15, 16, 17, 18 and 19.)

The company's insurer or broker may be able to present relevant information in support of the case law. However, insurers have remarkably few detailed data in this field readily available but a special survey may be of assistance, particularly if the insurer has its own risk management department.

## In-house Product Information

Just as it is necessary to gather information about the product from outside the company, it is also necessary to carry out a similar exercise within the company. The obvious is too often overlooked because it is there every day, like the postman in the Father Brown story. It was said of one company, 'It did not have 20 years' experience in the production of a certain product line... it had two years' experience, ten different times'. The company went on making the same mistakes time after time and failed to learn from its experiences.

In-house product information relating to safety will be available only if a determined attempt is made to collect it. Each function should maintain a file on product safety as a matter of course. An alternative, in a bigger organisation, is to apply the services of an information scientist or the technical library to maintaining such information.

A valuable source will be complaints received by the company. These should be regularly collated, analysed and circulated to top management. The analysis should be carried out in a manner that exposes the cause of the complaint. If the product is implicated the defect that caused the complaint should be ascribed to one of three possible sources: design, manufacturing, or failure to instruct or warn. Another source of information is the reports of service engineers. These should be treated in a similar manner to complaints.

An in-house information review should be prepared by each function on the safety record of previous products and form part of the support data of the Product Design Specification.

## Reliability

Reliability is defined as 'the ability of an item to perform a required function under stated conditions for a stated period of time'. The reliability requirements of the new product have an important place in the Product Design Specification, for these may influence the safety of the product. Some type of reliability specification (eg BS 5750 *Guide to reliability and main-tainability programme management*) will be needed if the trade-off with maintainability is to be achieved without affecting product safety. This can be a difficult area to chart and at the Product Design Specification stage it may be an advantage to allow some flexibility.

At a later stage in development more specific information will become available from feasibility testing, evaluation testing and environmental testing. Safety-critical parts can be identified so that particular attention can be paid to them in the design process. These will be the parts that would lead to conditions hazardous to the user if they should fail. In some products it may be possible to weight different parts according to their potential danger.

## Packaging, Warehousing and Distribution

With some sensitive products packaging, warehousing and distribution can be important to product safety. There are a number of EEC Directives concerned with dangerous substances which have been implemented in full or in part by Classification, Packaging and Labelling of Dangerous Substances Regulations 1984 (Statutory Instrument 1244). Another example is concerned with materials and articles in contact with food or drink under The Materials & Articles in Contact with Food Regulations 1978. It may be necessary for the Product Design Specification to deal with aspects such as these.

The overall design may have to accommodate specific packaging constraints. In one instance, catamaran hulls exported overseas had to be shipped by container, so that the container size determined hull dimensions for safe distribution. Vibration or shock during warehousing and distribution could affect safety-critical parts unless they are packed adequately.

## Scientific and Technological Breakthroughs

If the Product Design Specification requires new scientific or technological knowledge then uncertainty in incorporating the unknown into the product has to exist. If the design has to take such a path then the affected section of the final design should be allocated special risk analysis techniques during the design process. It may be an advantage to incorporate into the Product Design Specification alternatives of known capabilities as a back-up if the novel design produces unacceptable risks.

## Other Factors

Product safety apart, a Product Design Specification should be a considerable document. An idea of the factors that can be involved is gained from the following:

| | |
|---|---|
| Performance | Size and weight |
| Quantity and manufacture | Aesthetics, appearance |
| Maintenance | Materials |
| Environment | Product life span |
| Politics | Competition |
| Standards and specifications | Quality and reliability |
| Ergonomic aspects | Shelf life |

| Customer | Process |
| --- | --- |
| Time Scale | Testing |
| Target product cost | Company constraints |
| Packaging | Marketing constraints |
| Shipping | Patents |

The danger is that product safety will be swamped by the many important activities that are needed to develop a new product. Unfortunately product safety is not glamorous; to most non-technical people it can be a negative concept. It must be established as an activity in its own right with its own rightful demands on resources.

## DESIGN REVIEW SYSTEMS

The manner in which a company organises the management of product design is very much an individual matter, but it will have an important part to play in the risk reduction programme.

One approach used in the electronics industry is to have six Design Reviews which each consider the following twelve points:

| Reliability | Product test | Safety |
| --- | --- | --- |
| Performance | Interchangeability | Ergonomics |
| Maintenance | Installation | Appearance |
| Manufacture | Simplicity | Cost and value |

The first review is the Design Concept Review, which is held before the development work commences and all the specifications and procedures have been established. The second review deals with the design approach and unit specification, the design verification test specification and the reliability test programme. The next four Design Reviews, accompanied by the appropriate checklist, will cover unit design, experimental data and value analysis, documentation and manufacturing planning and the Final Design Review.[1]

Another approach, from a different direction, is to be found in a Defence Standard[2], which dates back to 1973. The Standard gives the requirements of a contractor's quality control system and identifies the elements of a system to be designed, established and maintained to ensure that the contract requirements are met. The design and development programme will include:

— code of design practice and procedures

— investigation of new techniques

— preparation and maintenance of drawings and specifications

— specification of manufacturing processes

— the evaluation of new material

— control of reliability and value engineering

— establishment of design review procedures

— use of defect/data feed-back.

A more modern view is in a NATO document[3], where the part dealing with design and development control says

The contractor shall establish and maintain control of design and development functions wherever performed including the identification and control of their interfaces with other functions. Such a control shall include, but is not limited to, the provision where necessary of a design and development programme, a code of design practice and procedures, and be applied to the investigation of new techniques; the preparation and maintenance of drawings and specifications, including control of physical and functional tolerances to avoid the use of irrational limits and to ensure interchangeability; the specification of manufacturing processes; the evaluation of new *matériel* under appropriate environmental conditions; reliability and maintainability tasks; value engineering tasks, the establishment of design review procedures to ensure progress towards the achievement of the design and development programme objectives through the timely identification of problem areas; the use of defect data feedback from previous designs when appropriate; the transition from the design and development phase to the manufacturing phase. Before release the engineering data developed for purchasing, manufacturing, inspection, installation purposes, etc, shall be verified for accuracy, stage of completeness and conformance to contract requirements.

Another view[4] examines the factors needing particular attention to reduce design defects and recommends ensuring that

— designers employed on specific tasks are capable of carrying them out effectively

— the overall product specification is used as the control as the design evolves

— the designer has adequate information sources at his disposal

— specialist help is available to the designer, who cannot be expected to master everything

— production engineers are included in design teams to cover the design/production interface

— adequate development and testing facilities are available for prototype work and the evaluation of part designs

— regular design reviews are carried out and that designs are audited

— there is effective co-ordination

— results of defect analysis are fed back to the designer.

A major company, much concerned with ensuring that the design of its products is as safe as possible, has adopted a special procedure for design review and design change. The following is an outline of the procedure used.

For new products the objectives are

1 To ensure that

— they can demonstrably meet design criteria and functional requirements: they are safe to use

— all documentation, including drawings, specifications, literature etc are to the highest standard and accurately reflect the manufacturability and performance of the product

  — there is a smooth handover from development to manufacturing.

2 To provide a documented procedure for deciding whether changes to the design of existing products or extensions to existing product ranges should be submitted to a full design review.

3 To ensure that the company develops safe, reliable products, take all reasonable steps to reduce anticipated product liability exposure to a minimum, and provide a sound documentary basis for defence in the event of any claim challenging the performance or safety of company products.

For new products at least two design reviews are held before the product is launched, which are

1 Prototype reviews. The purpose is to understand the extent to which the current design meets the defined design and performance criteria; and to decide if the prototype design is acceptable for delivery to the customer for testing for a particular purpose. Prototypes which are accepted by the review as suitable for customer testing are released under a Development Product Release Certificate signed by the project leader. This states that the product has not been subject to qualification testing and that no warranty of performance is offered for any particular application; responsibility for experimental testing lies with the customer who undertakes to indemnify the company against any liability, claims or damages that might arise therefrom.

2 Final Design Review. The purpose is to decide whether

  — the product design is complete, meets all the applicable performance criteria both internal and external and is ready for market launch

  — any limitations of the product design are clearly understood and documented

— all drawings, specifications, manufacturing and inspection procedures have been raised and approved to ensure manufacture of the product with consistent quality

— all documentation and literature to ensure the correct and safe use of the product has been raised and approved.

All new products must be approved at a Final Design Review before they can be released for general sale. If normal production samples are not available before the Final Design Review, then full product qualification must be carried out on the first production run. If the production samples fail qualification a further design review must be convened.

For existing products all changes to established designs are processed through a document change system, which ensures that the impact of the change is reviewed. In certain specified cases the changes are submitted to a full design review.

A new design which is merely an extension of an existing product range would probably not require a full design review, but the basis for such a decision has to be fully documented and filed.

The design reviews are for decision making and not for information transfer, so those attending must have the appropriate level of authority. The following functions should be represented: marketing, sales, manufacturing, technical development, product management, quality, product safety, and appropriate divisional senior managers.

Events occurring and decisions made at design reviews are recorded in the Design Review Log and filed in the project file. The log provides evidence that specific topics were discussed during the design stage and documents the reasons for decisions that were made. Such evidence can be of considerable value in substantiating the defence to a challenge to the safety of a product. In addition it provides useful background information when assessing the effect of subsequent proposed changes to the design. (See Case History 2.)

## BRITISH STANDARD 5750

This Standard is concerned with the system for the assurance of quality, rather than the product itself. It is divided into three parts of which the first is relevant.

Part 1. Specification for design, manufacture and installation. This specifies the quality system to be applied when the technical requirements of *matériel* and/or services are specified principally in terms of the performance required, or where design has not been established.

In these circumstances the supplier is frequently responsible for design, development, manufacture, installation work and field trials. Reliability and other characteristics can be ensured only by control of quality throughout all phases of this work.

The Standard is very wide ranging but does not include product safety in design as an activity in its own right.

The International Organization for Standardization has published a draft International Standard[5] which upgrades BS 5750. The part which deals with design review says

At the conclusion of each phase of design development, a formal, documented, systematic and critical review of the design results should be conducted. This should be distinguished from a project progress meeting, which is primarily concerned with time and cost. Participants at each design review should include representatives of all functions affecting quality as appropriate to the phase being reviewed. The design review should identify and anticipate problem areas and inadequacies, and initiate corrective actions to ensure that the final design and supporting data meet customer requirements.

The elements of design reviews include details of the items concerned with:

— customer needs and satisfaction

— product specification and service requirements

— process specification and service requirements.

## REDUCING THE RISKS OF A HAZARD

During the Design Review hazards will be identified and their risks assessed in terms of probability and severity, possibly using one of the techniques described in Chapter 7. The details of exactly how the risk of a hazard is tackled is outside the scope of this book, for it is not concerned with the nuts and bolts of safety. However, broadly speaking, the risks of an identified hazard can be reduced by

— design

— safety devices

— instructions and warnings.

During the design review process it may be possible to design out an identified hazard by eliminating its cause or the frequency with which it will occur. Alternatively a safety device could be incorporated in the design to prevent the hazard causing injury or damage, such as a micro-switch or a magnetic brake to stop over-run and maintain control over energy. If a hazard is inherent in the fundamental design of a product it may be possible only to instruct or warn to reduce the possibility of injury or damage. Here, the instruction or warning should be part of the design process and not an afterthought to be added later. A warning cast into the metal body of a product will be far more permanent than a four-colour transfer stuck on in the finishing shop — and eventually painted over by the end-user. (See Case Histories 6, 9, 13, 14 and 18.)

Each industry will have its own specific design concepts which have been developed over a number of years, frequently by trial and error. Any check-list of design considerations for preventing hazards has to be very general; its main application will be for organising information and generating an approach to an identified problem. There are two great truths. The first is that there is no such thing as 'fail safe' in the absolute sense of the term. Totally 'fail safe' is an end that can never be fully achieved. The second great truth is summed up in 'Keep it simple, stupid' (KISS). Complicated safety systems can introduce their own hazards and perhaps create a false sense of safety.

## SUMMARY

There can be no one answer to the reduction of design-related hazards. A critical milestone, however, is a Product Design

Specification which is established as a result of a multi-functional input. A formal Design Review System has an important part to play in risk reduction, with identified hazards and assessed risks being reduced by design, safety devices or the use of instructions and warnings.

## REFERENCES

1   Lawlor, A J (1978) Quality assurance in design and development. *Quality Assurance*. London, Institute of Quality Assurance.

2   *Quality Control System Requirements for Industry* (1973). Defence Standard 05-21/Issue 1.

3   NATO Requirements for an Industrial Quality Control System (1984). *Allied Quality Assurance Publication*. Edition No 3.

4   Pugh, S (1979) Production and design — the division of responsibility. Oyez Seminar 'Design Liability in the Engineering and Manufacturing Industry'.

5   Quality Management & Quality System Elements — Guidelines (1985). Draft International Standard ISO/DIS 9004. International Organization for Standardization, Geneva.

# CHAPTER 9

# Risk Transfer Programme for Product Design

However good the risk reduction programme some residual risk will always remain. The perfectly safe product can never be designed. A key element of the overall strategy is the transfer of some of these residual risks to a third party. The principal ways of doing this are by contract, insurance and compensation schemes.

## CONTRACT CONDITIONS

For our purposes a company has two types of contract: one for the purchase of incoming goods and another for the sale of its end-product.

Where no written contract exists certain requirements are implied by legislation. For example, the goods have to be of merchantable quality under the Sale of Goods Act 1979, see Chapter 1. But it is advisable to support and extend these conditions, especially in a climate of strict liability in tort.

If a purchased component is defective it can make the end-product defective, and cause its manufacturer significant problems in the market-place. In such a case it is important to know where the liability will lie. If the design of the component was formally accepted by the end-product manufacturer then there can be no recourse against the component supplier for a design defect. But if the component supplier recommended his design as suitable for the end-product manufacturer's purpose, then he will have some liability.

In practice circumstances are not always so clear cut. The design of a component will often be the result of a dialogue between the supplier and the purchaser. Design engineers may be certain who was responsible for the final specification, but unless this is borne out by the documentation they could have difficulty in proving their view in the event of a serious incident.

The car industry is one where responsibility for defective bought-in components has been developed, as the following example shows. The Swedish car maker, Volvo, recalled 48 000 cars in 1984 for minor repairs to the generator cable to prevent insulation systems from overheating. Included in the recall were about 30 000 turbo-charged cars sold mainly in the United States, Canada, Japan and Puerto Rico during the previous three years. No serious faults developed and the cost of the adjustments was passed on to the manufacturers of the components that did not meet Volvo's specification.[1]

A purchasing contract is used to regulate such things as price, quantity, method of payment and delivery, and certain contingencies, such as strikes, political embargoes and war, which could make performance of the primary contractual obligation impossible. It may specify the remedies that should be involved if something goes wrong with the arrangements.

Standard form contracts are used by parties with strong bargaining powers. The weaker party often cannot shop around for better terms, because the supplier may have a monopoly like a nationalised utility, or because everyone in the same field uses the same clauses, for instance those formulated by professional or trade associations.

The advantage of the standard form is that time and expense are saved in negotiating separate agreements. Difficult risks can be excluded and certain contingencies accommodated, as happens with insurance contracts. The company using the standard form has the advantage of excluding undesirable consequences, often by transferring them to someone else. The variables are reduced to a minimum. But the growth of disclaimers and exclusion clauses has changed the balance, especially as mounting interest has enhanced the prominence of product liability.

The development of social welfare brought into focus a realisation that superior bargaining powers could operate against the public interest. In some circumstances the end-user may not actually agree to the terms of a standard form at all and then his only choice would be to take it or leave it.

A survey of 51 firms in England[2] showed that they fell into two distinct groups: the business to business companies and the financial institutions. The first group, involved in commercial operations, did not commonly use exclusion clauses as opposed to limitation clauses in their contracts. Those that did use exclusion clauses tended to prevent liability arising on the part of a supplier because of specified causes beyond the individual's control, such as strikes, non-availability of materials and government action.

Limitation clauses and procedural clauses, such as arbitration provisions, were more common. Some firms limited liability in contracts of supply to a particular sum, usually a multiplier of the contract price. This was justified, particularly among component manufacturers, on the ground that it was regarded as commercially unacceptable to incur liability for consequential loss.

Many light engineering firms in the survey made components, each of relatively small value, under sub-contracts. The price paid per unit, often on a royalty basis, was considered so small (in relation to the risks likely to be incurred if the manufacturer undertook liability for consequential losses) that it was considered reasonable to limit liability to a multiplier of the contract price.

The alternative of insurance had been considered by some of the firms, but the premiums demanded were regarded as an unjustifiable expense, if the end-product manufacturer was prepared to take the risk upon himself. However, for most specially negotiated contracts for complex equipment, as in the electronic, medical or aircraft fields, the end-product manufacturer took out extensive insurance cover.

In these cases the exclusion or limitation clauses passed on those risks which the insurance company had refused to cover, or would do so only at an unacceptably high premium. One insurance company would only offer cover to contractors where the contract price exceeded £1 million, and if it had the right of veto on the contractual terms.

Apart from the above, most businesses were insured against surprisingly few risks. Very few were insured against loss of production as a result of deliberate in-house sabotage. In most other respects small manufacturers appeared to be their own insurers. A reason for using exemption and especially limitation clauses was the desire to avoid court proceedings, and also a distrust of lawyers', and particularly judges', ability to understand the problems of people in business.

A large number of contracts in the engineering industry used forms containing standard conditions of sale or purchase. The buyer would order in accordance with his conditions and the seller would acknowledge with his printed conditions. The significance of the exact correspondence between offer and acceptance escaped many of the businessmen consulted in the survey.

Some clauses try to excuse the defendant from any liability incurred as a result of his breach, but the form is by no means conclusive. Limitations of liability or remedy restrict the exercise of a right or remedy arising out of the breach of any obligation in the contracts. Time clauses are usually designed to limit the time within which suit must be brought. Some limitation clauses may attempt to alter the onus of proof of matters under the contract, or provide that one matter is to be treated as conclusive evidence of another.

Certain types of exclusion clauses are declared absolutely void by statutes, some of which give the courts a discretion to control exclusion clauses. By far the most important is the Unfair Contract Terms Act 1977 discussed in Chapter 1, which brought in the test of reasonableness for exclusion clauses concerned with liability for negligence for personal injury in non-consumer contracts. It provides that in consumer contracts for the sale and supply of goods all exclusion clauses concerned with liability for negligence for personal injury are void.

The term 'battle of the forms' is used to describe the situation where a manufacturer sends to a supplier a standard form of contract — possibly part of his order form — which says that the contract is on his terms. The supplier replies by returning *his* standard form — probably part of *his* acceptance note — saying that the contract is on his terms. Often both standard forms will contain exclusions.

There are a number of results from this situation

— a contract on the manufacturer's terms

— a contract on the supplier's terms

— a contract on terms implied by common law

— a contract on terms common to both standard forms or

— no contract at all.[3]

A company's conditions of sale are also important in the transfer of liability. Someone downstream of the factory gate could cause a product to become defective, even though its original design and manufacture were perfectly satisfactory. This could be caused by improper storage conditions, temperature cycling, vibration during distribution, unauthorised modifications, improper installation, etc. One of the ways in which some of these liabilities can be transferred is by contract and the remarks above regarding purchasing contracts apply.

The following clauses are taken from actual conditions of sale, but their inclusion does not imply that they would be upheld in court. Indeed, a number will be struck down by the Unfair Contract Terms Act, see Chapter 1:

— Seller gives no warranty express or implied as to description or any other matters.

— Any claim must be made within 14 days from the delivery of the goods and any claim not so made shall be absolutely barred.

— No warranty whatsoever is given as to the quality of the goods or as to their fitness for any purpose and the conditions implied under Sections 13 to 15 of the Sale Of Goods Act are hereby excluded.

— All conditions, warranties and liabilities implied by statute, common law or otherwise are excluded.

— All implied warranties and conditions as to quality, condition or fitness for any purpose of the goods are hereby expressly excluded.

— We shall not be responsible in any event for loss of profits or for any other consequential loss whatsoever arising from defects in the manufacture of our goods.

— The seller's liability for damages arising out of any claim, whether made in tort or in contract, shall in no event exceed the purchase price of the delivery in respect of which such claim is made.

— The above conditions cannot be varied, suspended or added to and they shall override any conflicting terms in the purchaser's order.

— Any claim by the buyers on account of quality shall be decided by reference to and on the basis of control samples held by the sellers and the results of the examination of such samples shall be conclusive in all respects with regard to such claim.

Contract conditions are often drawn up with commercial considerations in mind and with little or no thought for product liability. It is not unusual to discover that they have merely been copied from the conditions of another company or prepared by someone with no appreciation of the legal consequences.

As we have seen in Chapter 3, the introduction of strict liability in tort will make void some clauses which seek to exclude liability, whether caused by design or not, so that the consequences of a design defect can be very serious indeed. The defect can be imported into a company by a component or caused after the end-product has left the factory gate. In either case the contract conditions could be critical in the allocation of liability.

## INSURANCE

In simple terms a risk is insurable if it can be properly identified, precisely defined, and quantified in words and figures for probability and severity. The insurer will put the risk alongside other similar ones and make a 'book' on the underwriting probabilities. The premium he charges, to accept the transfer of the risk, will reflect his assessment of it. The greater the probability and severity, and the more difficult the risk is to define, the higher will be the premium. Some risks are not insurable and some only at penal rates, while other high-risk areas, such as aviation or pharmaceuticals, can only be placed in limited specialist markets.

The insurer has a number of variables he can employ to adjust his exposure, apart from the premium itself. A deductible (or excess) is an amount or percentage, specified in the policy, which is deducted from partial loss claims. The insured may have to pay the first £100 000 of any claim under a product liability policy; which means in fact that he, the insured, retains that part of the risk. An aggregate is the maximum amount that the underwriter will pay under the terms of a policy in a given period of time, whatever the claims made; for example, not more than £500 000 in a particular year.

Another method by which an underwriter seeks to protect himself from some of the management risks is by percentage participation. An example of this would be that when a claim was paid a proportion of the loss would remain uninsured (perhaps 10 per cent) and this amount would have to be met by the insured. Loosely, it is an across-the-board deductible.

One of the most important changes in the insurance market is an alteration in the terms of cover from 'claims occurring' to 'claims made'. This has considerable importance for the designer, especially when a design defect only comes to light after a period of use reveals its existence. An example is found in claims arising from a disease caused by long term exposure to a harmful substance, such as asbestos. If a company puts a product containing asbestos on the market it may be claimed, many years after the original supply, that injury had been caused.

A product liability policy written on an 'occurrence form,' one that was in force when the damage or injury originally happened, would respond to such a claim. Where damage occurs over a period of time policies in force in different years may all be called upon to respond to these claims, possibly involving a number of different insurers.

The fundamental point for the designer is that a policy written on an occurrence form will respond to an occurrence happening during the period of insurance, without any reference to when the loss is discovered or when any claim is made by a third party. Most policies have a condition which ensures that the insured has to report any loss as soon as he becomes aware of it, but it is a feature of liability insurance that the injury or damage which results in a claim may be caused years before it becomes apparent. This is called the latent damage exposure.

The advantage of the claims occurring basis for the designer is that, should latent damage occur, the policy in force at the time will respond and provide cover in the future. A major disadvantage is that, if a claim is made 10 or 20 years after the occurrence, the limit of indemnity of the policy may not be adequate in relation to current court awards. Further, it may be that in the interim no insurance was purchased, the insurer has gone out of business or records have been lost.

From the insurer's point of view the major disadvantage of the occurrence form is that, once the policy is written, it is impossible to establish when the liabilities arising from it are extinguished. In the United States the combination of the occurrence form and latent damage, coupled with the legal system, produce nothing short of catastrophe for some sectors of the liability market.

The claims made form takes a fundamentally different approach to the occurrence form. The claims made form means that a liability policy will only respond to claims actually made during the period of the policy, regardless of when the event that gave rise to the damage occurred; usually there will be a retroactive date.

The advantage of the claims made form for the designer is that the limit of indemnity is more likely to be adequate for current conditions, without having to guess what would be required in 10 or 20 years' time. The disadvantage arises mainly when continuous cover cannot be maintained from year to year. If there is a break in cover, or the insurers will not renew, the designer will be at risk for incurred but not reported claims from previous years.

For the insurer the claims made form has the major advantage of shortening the uncertainty of liability business. It responds in the year that claim is notified and cover ceases once the current policy is completed. The risk of aggregation of limits of indemnity is removed, because only the current limit of indemnity applies. At the end of any policy year the insurer can amend the terms of coverage to eliminate further claims for particular types of damage; indeed, it would be possible to cancel the coverage altogether, so eliminating any further liability for the particular insured.

With an occurrence form, even if the policy is cancelled, the insurer will still be liable if claims arise in the future for damage which occurred during the policy period. With the claims made form this problem is very largely eliminated.

The liability insurance market has no common approach to the move towards claims made covers. The designer should be well aware of this change in risk transfer. He should realise that once the liability moves to a claims made form it becomes difficult if not impossible to revert at some future date to an occurrence form, because, unless a future occurrence form insurer were prepared to give a retroactive cover, a gap in cover would be opened up. This gap would be in respect of future claims made relating to occurrences during the claims made policy period.

The chief way in which an insurer will control his exposure is in his wordings, his contract conditions. These are the statements in the policy which set out what is covered and what is not, including specific exclusions which may vary with individual risks. There are numerous different wordings, each dealing with defined areas of risk, such as life, motor, marine, aviation, property, fraud and so on.

There is no one policy which deals with design, because the effect of a design defect can be revealed in a number of different ways depending on the risks it presents. For example, if a design defect resulted in the product causing injury to a user, product liability insurance would provide cover to meet such a legal liability. A design defect could cause a product to fail to do the job for which it was bought, without injuring anybody, and here product guarantee cover would be the appropriate transfer mechanism. A third party could suffer financial loss because of the design defect in a product and financial loss insurance would provide indemnity. A major product recall could be required if a design defect in a product made it sufficiently dangerous, and product recall insurance cover may respond. A design engineer who was guilty of professional negligence in the course of his work could find protection under professional indemnity cover.

For each type of cover it is necessary to examine the exact wording in order to be clear about precisely what is covered. Further, it is at times unwise to look at one particular cover in isolation, as one may interlock with another — public liability and product liability, for instance. Deductibles and aggregates will also affect the degree of cover provided.

Before a design defect can trigger a particular policy to respond, it may be necessary to be certain that a design defect *is* the cause. A manufacturing error may be traced to a poorly designed product, which did not give production a reasonable chance of replicating it without fault. Alternatively, an inadequate instruction or warning could be the cause of a fault which was wrongly blamed on a design error.

A brief description of the chief types of insurance policies is given below.

**Product Liability Insurance.** This insurance is designed to protect the insured company against its legal liability for injury to third parties, caused by goods which the insured has sold, supplied, serviced or repaired. Liability can arise under statute or common law, and can be incurred outside the country where the goods are manufactured. Product liability insurance is usually offered in conjunction with public liability insurance. In these cases perhaps 90 per cent of the premium may be accounted for by the product risk, and only 10 per cent by the public liability for a manufacturer with no unusual exposures. Most general insurers write product liability business and will provide cover for the insured's legal liability for accidental bodily injury and/or accidental loss or damage to material property caused by a product.

Insurers have a fairly precise definition of what they mean by the product that gives rise to the loss, and some exclude liability where the goods are still under the insured's control. A claimant's costs and expenses will be met where the insured is legally liable and so will the insured's own legal fees if they have been approved by the insurer. Territorial limits will be specified, for even 'world wide' cover will have important excluded areas. The policy will have clauses to limit the indemnity. The term 'insured' usually takes in the insured's personal representatives, and certain wordings include in the definition the names of principals for whom the insured is carrying out work. There will be a definition of what the insured's 'business' includes and what it excludes.

A standard policy will not provide indemnity for any damage to the goods themselves, nor for the cost of putting right such products, nor for recalling products. Some insurers may not accept liability for faulty design or instructions, nor will they provide cover where an insured has accepted liability by contract or agreement which would otherwise not have been incurred. High-risk products, eg aircraft, may be excluded and many policies also exclude the results of deliberate acts. All wordings exclude claims associated with war or nuclear events.

Extensions or endorsements will be used to modify the range of cover provided by a standard policy. Most policies require the insured to exercise reasonable care in loss prevention and to give the insurer written notice of any impending prosecution or injury. A clause prevents the insured from admitting liability, or making a payment in connection with a claim, without the insurer's agreement and, if it so wishes, the insurer will conduct any proceedings on behalf of the insured.

**Product Guarantee Insurance.** Cover is provided for the liability for the replacement or repair of products which are defective or fail to do the job for which they are intended. This cover can be extended to protect against other risks, such as product recall and pure financial loss, not occasioned by death or injury to persons, or damage to property — the standard operative clause of the basic legal liability wording.

**Financial Loss Insurance.** An indemnity is provided against a legal liability to compensate for consequential or financial loss suffered by a third party purely because a product was defective, or did not function as intended. It does not depend on injury or damage. To a limited degree it is possible to extend a public and product liability policy to include financial loss.

**Product Recall Insurance.** Few underwriters or brokers are involved with this risk and, perhaps it is true to say, even fewer have any conception of what the risk is all about. The object of recall insurance is to indemnify the policy holder for payments for specified expenses incurred in the withdrawal of declared products.

Some areas that may not be protected are: improper, inadequate or faulty formulae or design; breach of warranties of fitness, quality, efficacy and efficiency; withdrawal of kindred products; the cost of destruction of the recalled product; and the redistribution or replacement of the recalled product.

**Professional Indemnity Insurance.** The cover protects a professional person (engineer, architect, accountant, designer, doctor, pharmacist, lawyer, insurance broker) against his legal liability to pay damages to persons who have sustained loss arising from his own professional negligence, or that of his employees. Any person who practises a profession and holds himself out as competent to give advice or assistance, must exercise that degree of care which one is entitled to expect from any other competent practitioner in the same profession. If the degree of care falls below this standard an action for damages will liè based on negligence. When a design or formulation defect is the cause of the failure of a product, it may be necessary to look to professional negligence insurance (a product liability policy may exclude design or formulation from its cover) or errors and omissions insurance.

To obtain adequate insurance protection expert advice is needed, especially as the penalty for putting a defective product on the market is increasing all the time. A word of warning is necessary: expert advice is not as easily come by as may be expected. Some brokers do not have either knowledge or experience of this complex field, and may offer one of the standard policies, without understanding the need to tailor the overall product cover to meet the client's product exposure.

Insurance contracts are subject to the doctrine of utmost good faith, *uberrimae fides*. This is because they are different from other contracts in that only one party knows (or should know) all about the risk, and that is the proposer. The other party, the insurer, has to rely largely on the information given to him by the proposer. If one of the parties does not exercise the utmost good faith then the other can repudiate the contract.

It follows that it is the duty of the proposer to disclose all material facts relating to the proposed insurance. A material fact is one which would affect the judgement of a prudent under-writer and includes any communication made to or information received by the proposer (*Rivaz* v. *Gerussi 1880*). The proposer consequently has a positive duty of disclosure. Failure to disclose all material facts renders the contract voidable, even if the failure was inadvertent or even if the proposer honestly considered the facts to be immaterial.

It is very difficult to say what insurance will cost. Each risk has to be assessed separately and the premium will be influenced by the company's claims record, the products it sells and the countries in which it sells them. The capacity of the insurance market to underwrite risks will also be an important factor, and the availability of reinsurance will affect this.

Given these important qualifications Table 7, showing the cost of product liability insurance, will give a general picture. It was published in 1979 to 'represent no more than a tenuous indication of guide rates for a selected range of products'. An individual quotation would be needed to find out the current cost of cover, especially as the insurance market has changed greatly since the 1970s.

## COMPENSATION SCHEMES

Many countries have no-fault workmen's compensation schemes, including Canada, the United States and Australia. The problem of compensating the victims of defective products has been met in some countries by transferring the risk to a group of insurance and reinsurance companies. In 1974 New Zealand introduced the first comprehensive no-fault compen-sation scheme in the world for personal injury by accident.

Table 7 *Product liability insurance rates per mille*
*on turnover* *

| | |
|---|---|
| Domestic appliances | 0.60 – 3.00 |
| Electro-medical and X-ray appliances | 1.00 – 6.00 |
| Beverages (beer, mineral water, wines, spirits) | 0.15 – 0.70 |
| Burners, fuel oil | 0.50 – 2.50 |
| Bricks, stones, tiles | 0.10 – 0.50 |
| Bicycles | 0.15 – 0.90 |
| Plastics, plastic articles, colours, industrial fats and oils | 0.40 – 2.00 |
| Fertilisers | 0.30 – 2.00 |
| Pharmaceuticals | 0.50 – 6.00 |
| Clocks, watches | 0.10 – 1.00 |
| Textiles for clothes | 0.05 – 0.60 |
| Concrete | 0.20 – 2.50 |
| Construction plant | 0.50 – 3.00 |
| Woodworking | 0.15 – 1.50 |
| Explosives | 1.00 – 10.00 |
| Fodder | 0.40 – 3.00 |
| Footwear, leather goods | 0.10 – 0.60 |
| Furniture | 0.10 – 0.60 |
| Glasswear | 0.10 – 0.80 |
| Insecticides | 1.00 – 6.00 |
| Lifts | 0.50 – 2.50 |
| Machines, various | 0.50 – 3.00 |
| Office machines | 0.15 – 0.50 |
| Metal construction | 0.60 – 3.00 |
| Metal products | 0.15 – 3.00 |
| Packaging materials (except canning) | 0.10 – 1.20 |
| Pleasure boats | 0.30 – 1.00 |
| Sports goods | 0.10 – 1.00 |
| Toys | 0.30 – 0.75 |
| Transformers, turbines, generators | 0.50 – 3.00 |
| Motor cars (excluding recall) | 1.50 – 3.00 |
| Firearms | 0.30 – 1.00 |
| Rubber goods (except tyres) | 0.20 – 1.00 |

* Rates per thousand units of currency on turnover, eg £0.60 per £1000 or
$0.60 per $1000 and so on.

*Source:* European Committee of Insurance notes submitted by
Commissioner Davignon to the Legal Affairs Committee of the
European Parliament, 1 March 1979. *European Parliament Working
Documents. 17 April 1979.*

*Note:* See text, p 102.

In Sweden manufacturers and importers of drugs have voluntarily undertaken to pay compensation for drug-related injuries. The scheme is insured by a consortium of private Swedish insurers and no legislation is involved. Germany and Japan have special compensation schemes to help people harmed by drug defects. A law became effective in January 1984 in Switzerland concerned with non-occupational accidents (product-related and otherwise). Insurance is allocated through the Swiss national accident insurance fund or through authorised private underwriters, with compensation starting after three days of incapacity. The premium for the obligatory insurance cover is borne both by the employers and the employees.

## LIMITED LIABILITY

The incorporation of a company may not normally be thought of as a means of product risk transfer, but it can be seen in this way. A loss in excess of business assets will be transferred to the creditors of the business from its owners. Similarly incorporation transfers the risk from a few partners to many shareholders; entrepreneurs transfer risk to speculators; and on the Stock Exchange the buying and selling of shares includes the transfer of the product risk from the seller to the purchaser.

## SUMMARY

However good the risk reduction programme some residual risk will always remain. Defined parts of this residual risk can be transferred to third parties. The principal transfer mechanisms are contract conditions, insurance and compensation schemes, with limited liability providing minor support. Establishing adequate contract conditions and buying appropriate insurance cover to respond to a design defect, requires expert advice in order to give the designer maximum protection.

## REFERENCES

1   Report Worldwide (1984) *Product Liability International*. Colchester, Lloyd's of London Press Limited.
2   Yates, D (1982) *Exclusion Clauses in Contracts*. London, Sweet & Maxwell.
3   *ibid.*

# CHAPTER 10

# Risk Retention Programme for Product Design

The risk reduction programme will have minimised the design risks and the risk transfer programme will have moved part of the residual risks to third parties, but some of the latter will always remain. These have to be retained within the company.

In risk management terms there are two types of risk suitable for retention: those that occur frequently and cause small losses and those that occur infrequently with catastrophic losses. The first are represented by the small every-day complaints which inevitably arise in products made by the million, and the second by major aircraft catastrophes and industrial accidents.

A design risk may have to be retained for a number of reasons. The cost of further risk reduction may not be commercially practicable; or the state of the art such that it is not possible, whatever the financial circumstances; or probability estimates show that to attempt to do so would be unrealistic.

Relevant design risk transfer by the insurance mechanism may not be available because the company cannot afford the premiums involved, or an appropriate cover may not be available for the product concerned. An insurer may require such a large deductible before accepting cover that the company concerned feels that this is unacceptable, or the exclusion clauses in the wording may make the cover provided inadequate.

Design risks can accompany a bought-in component or sub-assembly, the failure of which can cause a dangerous defect in the end-product. The component supplier may be unwilling to accept, under the terms of the supply contract, full liability for the consequences of such a failure. The contract may limit the liability in a number of ways, for instance, to a maximum of a multiplier of the contract price or the value of the item supplied. Risk transfer in this case is of limited value so that risk retention has to be accepted for the major part of the residual risk.

The successful management of retained design risks depends on the establishment of an active programme in which they are dealt with in a positive manner. Some of the methods of doing this are discussed below.

## CAPTIVE INSURANCE COMPANY

This is created and owned by an organisation to insure the risks of its parent. The advantage is the formalisation of funding so that the reserves can be moved forward, year by year, with sufficient capitalisation to ensure solvency. There are: no acquisition costs; only one insured; no special organisation or offices required; profit is non-essential; investment income will discount premiums.

A company may find that a captive provides the answer if it cannot obtain the cover required on the insurance market, or if it cannot be obtained at an acceptable cost. A company that sets up its own captive demonstrates its confidence to carry part of its own risks, which could influence other insurers or reinsurers to take up a share.

A captive insurance company can be managed by its parents if it has the necessary experience or specialists can be recruited for the purpose. The usual method is to use outside managers such as underwriters, insurers, insurance brokers, lawyers, bankers or accountants. The skill of the management companies varies considerably.

It is important to remember that the formation of a captive does not bring independence from the insurance market. The part played by reinsurance becomes critical, for without it a captive would have considerable difficulty in spreading its risks.

Insuring in a captive is self-insurance, and the only real insurance is that part of the risk which the captive reinsures or co-insures. In effect it is a combination of risk retention and risk transfer.

In the USA the Liability Risk Retention Act 1986 allows the formation of a risk retention group, which is owned by its insured members comprising people, entities or companies with similar liability exposures. A risk retention group is a captive insurance company, for which the definition of liability can be very broad, which gains freedom from some regulation.

While the Act could make it easier for groups to use captives; the view of the reinsurers will still have a big influence on what can be covered and what cannot. Many professional managers do not see any great benefit from the formation of a risk retention group, because of the personal liability of experts and their managers; there is the benefit, however, of the avoidance of the joint and several liability between partners.

## DEDUCTIBLES

An insurer can avoid his liability for some losses by including a deductible in a policy. A simple deductible is a lump sum deduction from each claim. It is widely used to eliminate small claims with disproportionately high handling expenses. It is also a device to make the insured retain the first part of the risk himself.

For example, in a product liability policy the insurer may require a deductible of, say, £50 000. In effect the insured has to pay the first £50 000 of the cost of each incident to which the policy will respond. In fact, he retains this part of the risk. The amount over the deductible will be paid by the insurer, according to the cover provided by the policy, up to the maximum provided by the premium. This is the part of the risk that has been transferred to the insurer, according to the cover provided by the policy. If the costs are greater than the maximum, the insured will have to pay them himself, and this once more is risk retention.

A first loss cover is the mirror image of a deductible. Here the insurer pays for the loss up to the first loss limit and the insured has to pay the balance. So the insured transfers the first part of the risk and retains the balance.

## SPECIAL FUNDS

The fund is created by putting aside a sum each year and then drawing on it when a loss occurs. This spreads losses over a longer period. The fund must be readily converted into cash and carry sufficient reserve to absorb the wide fluctuations that might occur from year to year. The actuarial viability of a fund depends on the spread of risk which it is designed to retain. The sums put aside each year may not be tax deductible, and may not be accumulated, year on year, beyond a limited period; the losses themselves will be allowable tax expenses.

Another way to meet losses is by diverting funds from alternative uses. This has a disadvantage of having to forego the opportunity for which the fund was established, the possibility of having to turn assets into a liquid form at a disadvantageous time, and the possibility that insufficient capital will be available to cope with the loss and the demands of the business.

## SUMMARY

The remaining residual design risks are retained within the company by an active programme. Design risks may have to be retained because further risk reduction is not commercially practicable, or the state of the art is such that it is not possible, or probability estimates show that to attempt to do so would be unrealistic. The available methods include the creation of a captive insurance company, deductibles, first loss cover and special funds.

# PART 3

## CASE HISTORIES

# CASE HISTORY 1

## The *Amoco Cadiz*

At 9.45 am on 16 March 1978 the steering-gear of the tanker *Amoco Cadiz* broke down in rough seas, about ten miles from the Isle of Ushant, off Brest. The cause was the failure of a pipe flange on the main steering-gear hydraulic circuit which allowed the oil in the system to be discharged into the steering-gear compartment. The crew were unable to recharge the system and regain control of the steerage before the ship grounded at 21.04. Over the next few days the entire cargo of 226 000 tonnes of crude oil polluted hundreds of miles of the French coastline.

The steering-gear and related equipment of the *Amoco Cadiz* complied with all existing international regulations; which raised doubts about their adequacy. The disaster highlighted both the basic weakness of the single hydraulic circuit, almost universally employed in the ram and rotary vane types of steering-gear, and the drastic potential consequences of the failure of the steering-gear of a large tanker.

Following the *Amoco Cadiz* casualty new international regulations were developed as a matter of urgency for the steering-gears of all ships, but with particular emphasis on large tankers. The new regulations concentrated on the importance of maintaining the integrity of at least part of the hydraulic circuit after a single failure of pressure parts, so that steering capability could be maintained or be rapidly recovered after a fault. The regulations envisage automatic change-over of separate identical systems or means to separate automatically a single hydraulic circuit in order to isolate a fault in pressure parts.

The simple fault tree analysis, in Figure 4, of the type of steering-gear used in the *Amoco Cadiz* shows the route to failure in a qualitative manner direct through the OR gates. Figure 5 shows a fault tree analysis of a conventional four-ram steering-gear with six failure modes leading through the OR gates. Figure 6 shows a fault tree analysis of the same type of steering-gear designed in accordance with the new regulations, and fitted with

Figure 4 *Simple Fault Tree Analysis showing the route to failure of an Amoco Cadiz type steering-gear*

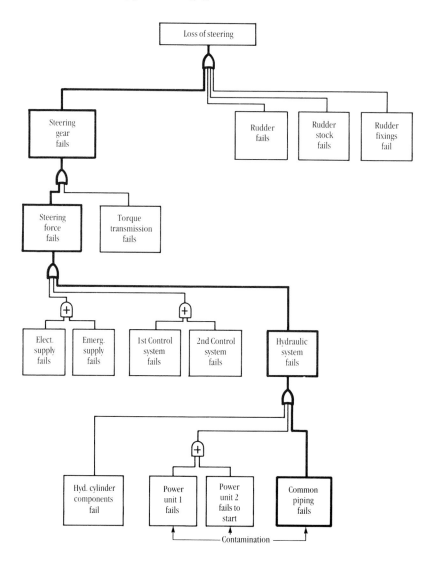

*Source:* Cowley, J (1982) 'Steering gear: new concepts and requirements.' *Trans. Inst. Mar. E.* Vol 94, Paper 23.

separate and independent power actuating systems, and shows the failure modes through the OR gates reduced to two. Fault tree analysis is explained in Chapter 7 (see pp 59-63).

The result of the grounding of the *Amoco Cadiz* was a series of complex international law suits which were consolidated into a single court action. A 111-page opinion was issued by Judge Frank McGarr of the Eastern Division of the Northern Circuit, Court of Illinois. He said, *inter alia*, that Amoco was entitled to damages against Astilleros, the Spanish shipyard which built the *Amoco Cadiz*, 'to the extent that its own liability was contributed to by the negligence and fault of the shipbuilder'.

The judge concluded that Amoco International Oil Company (AIOC), the operator, 'negligently performed its duty to ensure that the *Amoco Cadiz* in general and its steering-gear in particular were seaworthy, adequately maintained and in proper repair'.

He noted that AIOC 'negligently performed its duty to ensure that the crew of the *Amoco Cadiz* was properly trained', and failed in its duty to ensure that the design and construction of the *Amoco Cadiz* was 'properly carried out so as to result in a seaworthy vessel'. He said AIOC was negligent in operating the *Amoco Cadiz* without a redundant steering system, or any other means of controlling the rudder, in the event of the complete failure of the hydraulic steering system.

In arriving at his decision Judge McGarr outlined the history and operation of the *Amoco Cadiz*. These indicated there were problems with its steering-gear from the start which were not adequately comprehended or repaired. In addition the oil company did not follow the maintenance instructions for the steering-gear, which ultimately caused the disaster.

Judge McGarr listed several areas where AIOC failed to maintain the steering-gear of the *Amoco Cadiz* properly. The company did not act to ensure that the filters on the steering-gear were cleaned according to the instruction manual; it did not act to ensure that the oil in the steering-gear was changed; it did not arrange to have samples of the hydraulic fluid analysed; it did not require the ship's steering-gear system to be purged to remove air.

In addition he faulted the company for accepting the ship from the Spanish shipyard with acknowledged defects in its steering-gear. In particular the ship was delivered with cast-iron steering-gear ram bushings. It arranged to have bronze bushings

Figure 5 *Fault Tree Analysis of a conventional four-ram steering-gear, showing six failure modes through the OR gates*

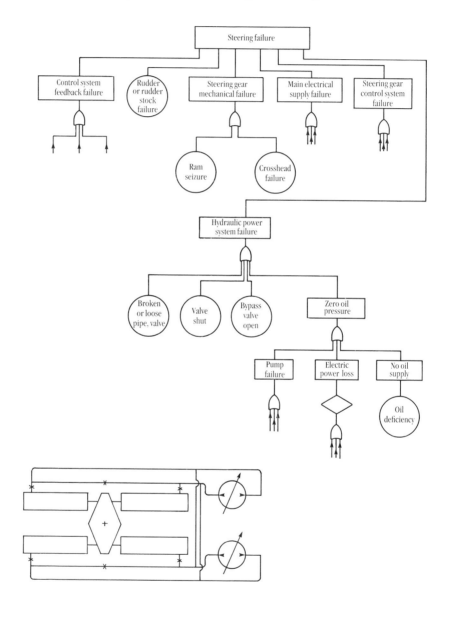

*Source:* Cowley, J (1982) 'Steering gear: new concepts and requirements.' *Trans. Inst. Mar. E.* Vol 94, Paper 23.

Figure 6 *Fault Tree Analysis of four-ram steering-gear with separate and independent power actuating systems showing two failure modes through the OR gates*

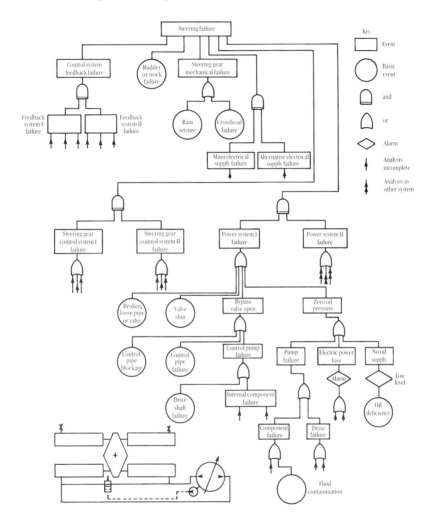

*Source:* Cowley, J (1982) 'Steering gear: new concepts and requirements.' *Trans. Inst. Mar. E.* Vol 94, Paper 23.

installed on its own vessels and placed additional bushings on board the *Amoco Cadiz*. These were not installed.

The judge noted that *Amoco Cadiz's* steering-gear in the last four months of its life was losing 7 to 12 litres of hydraulic fluid a day. This was 'greatly in excess of what would occur with a properly maintained system'. The report said, 'This excessive consumption was known to AIOC which in the exercise of ordinary skill and prudence, should have recognised it as symptomatic of a progressive degradation of the system's reliability.'

With both steering-gear pumps secured the *Amoco Cadiz* and her sister-ships experienced as much as 15 degrees of rudder movement while in port. 'This fact was well known among AIOC engineers and should have signalled a serious malfunction of the two-sided restrain system of the *Amoco Cadiz* steering mechanism.' The unexplained rudder movement of the *Amoco Cadiz* was not properly investigated and was not corrected. AIOC failed to instruct the *Amoco Cadiz* crew in emergency steering-gear drills and procedures to be followed in the event of a steering-gear breakdown.

## SOURCES

Cowley, J (1982) Steering gear: new concepts and requirements. *Transactions of the Institute of Marine Engineers* 94, p 23.
*The Financial Times* 21 April 1984.

# CASE HISTORY 2

## Nova Fritex Domestic Deep-Fat Fryer

A Belgian company Nova, part of ITT, manufactured a range of domestic appliances including a deep-fat fryer called Fritex. The product consisted of an aluminium casting, electrically heated by a separately manufactured element fused into the base of the main body as part of the casting. The product worked well and caused no problems, but the manufacture of the casting, with the inclusion of the heating element, was difficult and costly. An independent consultant suggested that a channel should be cast into the base of the pan and the heating element clamped in as a separate operation. Production of this design started in August 1975, as Fritex 3.

Figure 7 *The cost-reduction design defect of the Nova Fritex*

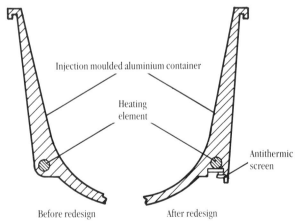

Injection moulded aluminium container

Heating element

Antithermic screen

Before redesign          After redesign

© *Quality Assurance* June 1978.

On 6 January 1976 Nova after-sales received a defective Fritex from a customer. Investigation showed that the heating element had moved in its groove sufficiently to allow one of the ends to contact the aluminium casting. A test confirmed that this was a potentially repeatable failure. On 10 January a second customer complained that he had received electric shocks from his Fritex. Production was stopped and a recall was instituted.

An assessment of the Fritex 3 showed that it had two design defects. First, the thermal contact between the heating element and the aluminium casting was not as effective as in the previous design. This caused the heating element to reach a temperature about 180°C higher than previously. Second, the stresses caused by the excessive temperature and less firm clamping of the element allowed it to creep around the channel as it was switched on and off. But this did not necessarily make the Fritex dangerous. Clear instructions about the need for an earthed connection and the fitting of a three-lead flex should have protected the user from any short-circuit. Also the Fritex was sold with a standard European plug moulded on to the flex — the 'fail-safe' device. It was the Belgian kitchen that made the Fritex dangerous, as many do not have properly earthed outlets. The standard European three-pin plug could easily be forced into an unearthed two-pin outlet.

A risk analysis of Fritex 3 revealed that only 25 per cent of Belgian kitchens had an earth meeting legal standards, 25 per cent had a make-shift non-legal earth and 50 per cent had no earth at all. It was assumed that a short-circuited Fritex on a non-earthed outlet would give someone a shock sooner or later. It was estimated that about one per cent of users receiving electric shocks would require medical treatment.

Risk Analysis of Nova Fritex 3

|  | Min % | Max % |
|---|---|---|
| Fritexes expected to short-circuit | 25 | 50 |
| Kitchens with no earth | 50 | 75 |
| Short-circuits giving electric shock | 100 | 100 |
| Shocked users needing medical attention | 2 | 8 |
| Overall product of proportions | 0.25 | 3 |

At the time of the failure Nova was a small company with staff weaknesses in its quality and technical departments. The design change was proposed and tested by a consultant unfamiliar with the requirements of the ITT Product Qualification system. The purpose of qualification testing was to make sure that the product conformed to the requirement: 'No new product must be handed over to the customer until it has passed its Product Qualification.' Fritex 3 had been tested and approved by authorities in a number of number of countries. The Fritex case led to a major re-emphasis on Product Qualification in Nova and a complete review of testing of all new products and any modifications to designs.

## SOURCE

Groocock, J M, Clifton, P and Mueller, A K (1978) The recall of the Nova Fritex. *Quality Assurance*. London, Institute of Quality Assurance.

# CASE HISTORY 3

## Exploding Office Chairs

In the early 1980s there were a number of accidents caused by a design fault in adjustable swivel office chairs. The type involved had the seat mounted on a central column, with a gas-operated springing system to give up and down movement. The compressed gas cylinders contained a pressure of 40 bars, with a side-entry lever to control the vertical movement at a touch. The danger arose when the cylinder fractured at the point at which the lever entered, causing an explosion as the pressure was suddenly released.

Figure 8 *Exploding office chairs*

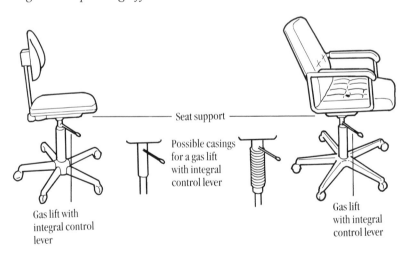

In Belgium such accidents had caused one death and several injuries. In the United Kingdom one victim sustained a smashed cheek bone and damaged eye socket. In Germany the first incidents were reported in 1982 in a Munich office and in the police headquarters in Dusseldorf. An employee of a Hanover bank examined a chair that had become unsteady; the cylinder fractured causing the seat to break off and a steel bolt was projected from the shaft into his head. In another accident the gas cylinder embedded itself in the ceiling.

There were more than 90 office chair manufacturers in Germany, and the majority made the adjustable swivel type; it was estimated that 2.4 million had been sold. In the United Kingdom the majority of the manufacturers used gas cylinders imported from Germany.

In Germany the first warning advertisements did not appear until 1984 and then joint action was taken by a number of interested bodies. The remedial action had to be paid for by individual owners of defective chairs, at a cost of DM35, due to a loophole in the law. Since January 1984 the only type of adjustment lever permitted for gas operated systems was top-entry; a new standard, DIN 4550/51, was introduced.

# CASE HISTORY 4

# Flixborough

Just before five o'clock in the afternoon of the first Saturday in June 1974, an explosion at the Nypro plant at Flixborough killed 28 people, injured about 90, and damaged 2000 houses and 167 shops and factories. Flames rose 200 feet into the air as the control building was reduced to rubble, killing the 18 men who were inside.

In the plant cyclohexane was being heated under pressure in six reactors, each of which was about 10m high and 3m in diameter. The reactors were usually connected in series but at the time of the explosion number five was out of commission; on 30 March it had been lifted off its platform by a crane and placed nearby. To keep the plant in operation reactor number four had been connected to reactor number six by a specially made bypass pipe.

The gap between reactor four and reactor six was about 6m and the outlet from reactor four was 0.35m higher than the inlet to reactor six. To accommodate these differences a dog-leg shaped pipe was made in the Nypro workshop. The bypass had bellows at each end to take up the expansion and contraction of the system. The six reactors together were 60m long and the difference in length between 0°C and the operating temperature of 150°C was 135mm. The bypass was fitted and tested — though not adequately — on 1 April.

After the explosion the bypass was found bent double on the concrete plinth below the reactors. The bellows at each end had torn apart, leaving 0.67m openings in each of the reactors through which the gas had escaped.

The subsequent Court of Inquiry found that in designing the bypass no-one had appreciated that the pressurised assembly would be subjected to a turning moment, imposing forces on the two bellows connections for which bellows are not designed. Neither had it been appreciated that the hydraulic thrust of the bellows would ten to make the dog-leg buckle at the mitre

Figure 9 *The bypass pipe in the Nypro plant, Flixborough*

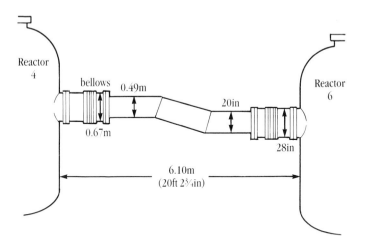

Figure 10 *The couple on the bypass pipe in the Nypro plant, Flixborough*

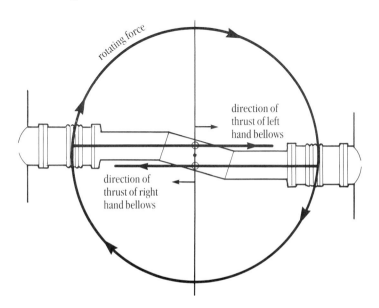

joints. No calculations were made to determine whether the bellows or pipe would withstand these forces. The relevant British Standard (BS 3351 1971) was not consulted, nor was the designer's guide issued by the bellows manufacturer; the complete bypass was not pressure tested before use to the safety valve pressure. BS 3351 requires the test pressure to be 1.3 times the design pressure.

In operation the forces on either end of the bypass were not opposite each other, because of the dog-leg shape necessitated by the difference in height of reactor four and reactor six. Each bellows exerted a force of 20 kilonewtons on its end of the bypass but they exerted a couple, which is a system of two equal but directly opposite parallel forces. This would have caused the bellows to 'squirm' (which happens when an accordion is played) and then to burst; parts of the bellows were found afterwards which had completely lost their corrugation. The combination of the forces exerted by the bursting bellows caused the pipe to jack-knife. This failure left the reactors open to the atmosphere and 40 tonnes of vapour were released to the atmosphere in 45 seconds.

## SOURCE

Marshall, V C (1979) *Disaster at Flixborough. Exeter,* A Wheaton & Son.

# CASE HISTORY 5

# Sprint Scissor Jack

The Consumer Safety Act 1978 empowered the Secretary of State to serve on any person a Prohibition Notice prohibiting that person from supplying, offering to supply, agreeing to supply, exposing for supply or possessing for supply goods which the Secretary of State considers unsafe.

On 11 October 1984 Alex Fletcher, the Minister with responsibility for Corporate and Consumer Affairs, served a Prohibition Notice on Sprint Motor Accessory Service Ltd of Ipswich forbidding further sales of its own brand Sprint Scissor Car Jack. The notice was to be enforced by Suffolk County Council. The reason for the notice was that it was considered that the jack was 'incapable of supporting the stated load and that its design can cause it to become unstable in use irrespective of the weight involved'.

> On Thursday 6th December 1984 I attempted to jack up the rear off-side wheel of my Datsun 120Y Sunny motor car using the jack. Because the operating handle was short I had to lie down partly under the car body and I found the handle and operating screw very stiff and hard to turn. I had applied the hand-brake and chocked the wheels. Before I judged the car to be raised high enough to remove the wheel the jack leaned over and the car fell off it, catching my right hand between the car body and the jack. I suffered minor cuts and was very alarmed. I retrieved the jack and lowered it. It was then seen to be bent over to one side. (From a statement made by a club steward in Exeter)

The Sprint had been imported from Taiwan and 35 000 had been sold in a year by the sole importer. On 30 January 1985 at Kingston-upon-Thames Magistrates Court Sprint were convicted of supplying

a Sprint 0.6TA Scissor Jack to which a false Trade

Description as to fitness for purpose was applied - printed on box, namely 'suitable for use on vehicles up to 1.25 Ton in weight' - Jack not suitable for purpose; contrary to Sect. 1 (1)(B) of Trade Descriptions Act 1968.

Figure 11 *Sprint scissor jack*

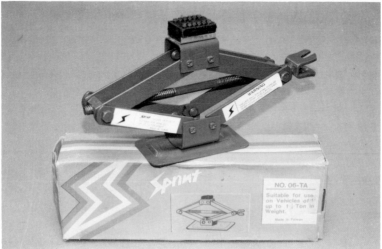

Warwickshire County Council

Sprint pleaded guilty and were fined £500 on each of two offences and were ordered to pay prosecution costs of £1000 and £100 in compensation.

# CASE HISTORY 6

## Brent Cross Crane Failure

A mobile crane was being used to erect a large Scotch derrick-crane, which was to work on the construction of the flyover which enables Hendon Way to cross the North Circular Road, near Brent Cross. The lorry-mounted mobile crane was just beginning to lift the king post of the Scotch derrick-crane when its jib collapsed sideways and fell on to a passing coach. The king post weighed 7.75 tons and seven people were killed and 32 injured. The Court of Inquiry published its findings in 1964.

The basic jib of the mobile crane consisted of two sections, each 15ft long, giving a jib of 30ft. Two extra jib sections, one of 20ft and one of 30ft, were available. By the use of the various sections jib lengths of 50ft, 60ft and 80ft could be obtained.

The 1962 Road Traffic Act imposed severe restrictions on the movement on a road of a vehicle having a forward projection of more than 6ft. To meet this requirement the basic jib of the mobile crane was hinged about its mid-point, so that its effective length could be halved for transit purposes.

The hinged section represented a discontinuity in the jib structure and thus was a potential source of weakness. To meet this, the designers placed it at the point of lowest stress, which was next to the top of the jib section. Design calculations were made for the use of additional jib sections inserted below the hinged section.

There was a failure to make sure that the crane owners were aware of the designers' intention: that the hinged section should always be inserted adjacent to the top section. In practice it was always inserted at the other end, adjacent to the bottom section, as this was more convenient.

The Court found that a major cause of the accident was the insertion of the hinged section in a position for which it was not designed. Immediately below the top section the bending force on it would have been less than a quarter of that obtaining at the lower position.

The Court found that the hinged section had not been manufactured as designed, and that there were a number of other contributing causes of a minor nature.

Figure 12 *Brent Cross crane jib*

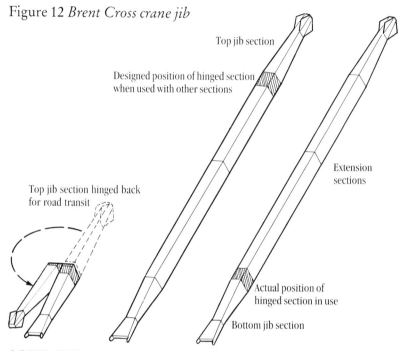

Top jib section

Designed position of hinged section when used with other sections

Extension sections

Top jib section hinged back for road transit

Actual position of hinged section in use

Bottom jib section

## SOURCES

Brent Cross Crane Failure. *The Engineering Designer*. November (1965) pp 4-6.
Report of the investigation of the crane accident at Brent Cross, Hendon, on 20 June 1964. London, HMSO, Cmnd 2760.

# CASE HISTORY 7

## DC-10 Engine Pylon

Aircraft No 110AA was a Series 10 DC-10 delivered to American Airlines on 28 February 1972. It became Flight 191 from Chicago to Los Angeles on Friday 25 May 1979, by which time it had completed 19 871 flying hours. Its last major overhaul had been on 30 March 1979 when No 1 engine and its pylon were removed as one unit by a fork-lift truck. The manufacturer's instruction manual specified 44 separate operations for such an activity. The removal of the engine and its pylon caused a crack on the rear mounting of the pylon about 20cm long, which subsequently lengthened to over 25cm. About ten seconds after take-off the aircraft lost its No 1 engine and the crash killed 273 people.

The Federal Aviation Authority (FAA) grounded all 138 DC-10s belonging to US operators for 37 days at a cost estimated at between $90m and $250m. The repercussions were immense and produced much comment and speculation in the media. After a six-month study the FAA concluded that the DC-10 engine pylon was fundamentally sound unless damaged during maintenance. But to deal with the maintenance 'damage tolerance' problem the FAA proposed compulsory modifications to the pylon attachment structure.

The proposals included the installation of two flush-fitting, instead of raised, bolts in a critical part of the area where the aft pylon bulkhead was attached to the wing torque-box mounting. The object was to reduce the possibility of the bulkhead attachment point striking protrusions if it was misaligned when offered up for connection. A mechanical handling device also reduced the possibility of misalignment and the titanium thrust-link was replaced by a stainless steel one.

In a separate action over matters brought to light by the DC-10 investigation, the FAA announced that it had fined McDonnell Douglas, the manufacturer of the aircraft, $300 000 as a civil penalty because the company had 'maintained a

Figure 13 *DC-10 pylon rear mount bulkhead*

**DC-10 pylon rear mount bulkhead**

Pre load indicator washer (PLI)

Pylon monoball mounting

Total 12

Impact cracks

$2\frac{3}{8}$ in  10 in  $\frac{5}{8}$ in

2 centre bolts to be recessed

Developed crack

PROPOSED FAA MODIFICATIONS

Front spar

Rear spar

5 ft  7 ft

Wing torque box

Replace titanium thrust link with stainless steel

Glass fibre rear fairing

FLIGHT INTERNATIONAL
J M

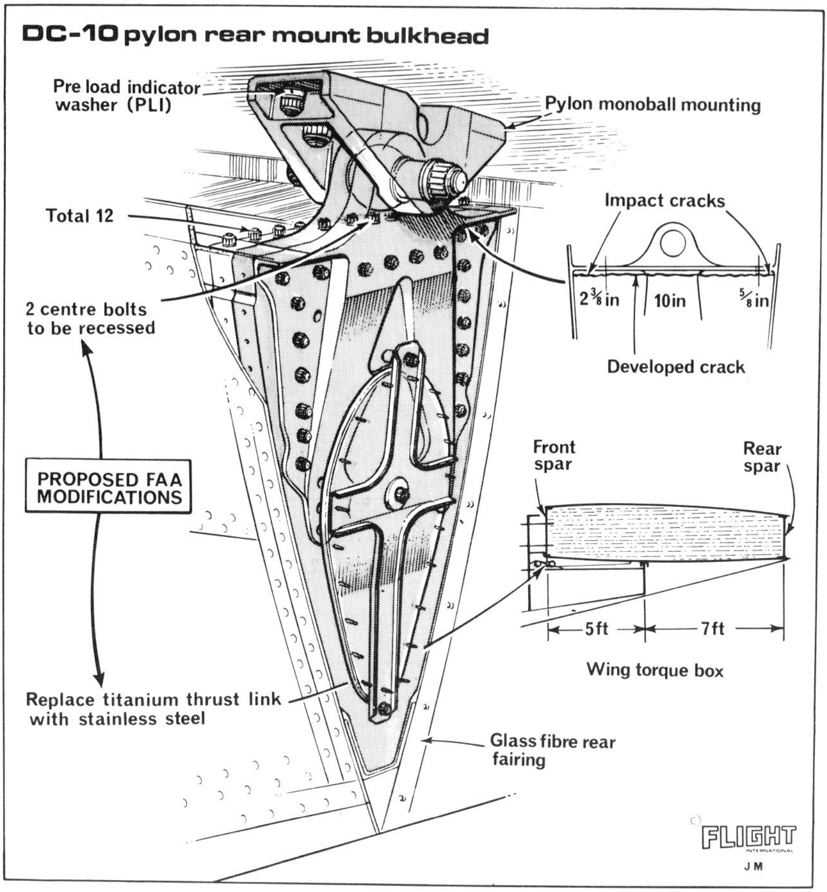

Flight International

defective quality assurance programme' in pylon production. It was emphasised that the production shortcomings were not a factor in the Chicago disaster.

## SOURCE

Air Transport *Flight International* 2 February 1980, p 293.

# CASE HISTORY 8

## DC-10 Cargo Door

The McDonnell Douglas DC-10 cargo door was secured by a latch. A torque tube revolves to drive a latch hook over its spool, while the top of the latch swings through an arc of about 90° until it comes to rest against the metal stop. Provided that the top part of the latch passes beyond the centre point of its arc, the force created by pressurisation (within the aircraft) will be transmitted to the door structure. A locking-pin system was incorporated to ensure that the top part of the latch actually did go over-centre.

In theory, if the latches were not fully home the locking-pins would jam and the resistance would be transmitted back to the handle on the outside of the door. In addition, the vent-door (which allowed access to the locking handle) would not close. Following a failure of a cargo door on a DC-10, McDonnell Douglas designed a support plate to prevent the torque tube distorting. This could occur if the handle on the outside of the cargo door was forced down. Furthermore, the linkages in the system were re-rigged so that the locking-pins would be driven further over the top of the latches.

Turkish Airlines Flight 981 took off from Paris at 12.30 pm on 3 March 1974 and headed for London. Turkish Airlines had been flying this particular DC-10 for over a year but the support plate which should have been fitted was missing, although there was something far more seriously wrong with the cargo door than this. Someone had misrigged the locking-pins so that even in the fully closed position they barely covered the lugs at all.

What in fact happened was that the travel of the pins was reduced, so that a child could have beaten the safety system. Even with the latches only partly closed, and with the locking-pins jammed up against them, it would only have needed a force of 13 lbs to operate the locking handle successfully, and close the vent door.

Figure 14 *DC-10 cargo door locking system*

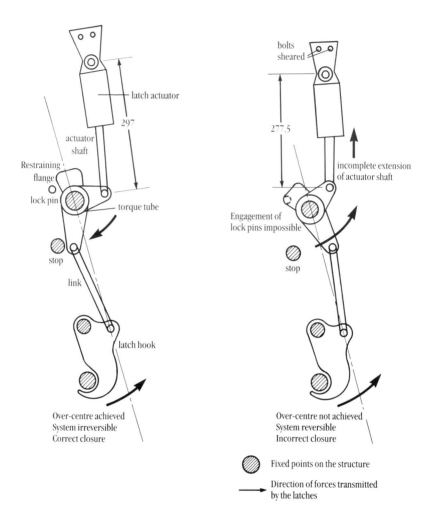

At Paris Orly Airport, Turkish Airlines used a private concern to provide it with ground service. A 39-year-old Algerian expatriate had been instructed how to close and lock the DC-10 cargo door. First, he had to activate the electrical power circuits and press a button which would bring the door down on its rubber seal. He held the button for a further ten seconds to give time for the actuators to move the latches over the spools on the door sill. He verified this by closing down the locking handle alongside the small vent door. If the latches were home the locking handle would move and the vent door would simultaneously close.

If the latches had not gone home the locking handle would encounter resistance and the vent door would not close. He did not understand the mechanics and neither could he read the instructions on the door, which warned him against using force on the locking handle, because they were printed in English. He thought he had to get the locking handle down and the vent door closed which meant it was safe. But because of the misrigging of the locking-pins the actuators had not driven the latches over the spool and, although the handle was down, the door was not safe.

At 11 500 feet, the pressure differential inside the DC-10 would have been 4.5 psi. There would have been almost five tons of air pressing against the inside of the door, competing directly against the ability of the partially closed latches to hold it shut.

Because the latches were not over-centre all of that force was transmitted to two bolts, a quarter of an inch in diameter, which held the latch actuator to the inside of the door. The bolts gave way, the latch talons were pulled from the spools and the door blew open, to be ripped from its hinges by the slip stream.

The crash was the world's worst up to that time, and 346 people died.

## SOURCE

Eddy, P, Potter, E and Page, B (1976) *Destination Disaster*. London, Hart-Davis, pp 313-21.

# CASE HISTORY 9

## Giraffe Site Placement Vehicle

During the formulation of the original product specification for the 'Giraffe' site placement vehicle it was decided to make it the safest vehicle on the market, from the viewpoint of stability. Since any handling device using forks relies upon gravity to retain its load, the risk to life and limb increases with height and reach, both in terms of the operator and people in the vicinity of the vehicle.

The first of this design in the field, it was decided to provide a system of operation such that any increase in the extension of the boom at a fixed elevation or, alternatively, depression of the boom at a fixed extension beyond predetermined limits, would automatically override the operator. He would be left with two options: either let the load remain at a position in space but still in safety, or shorten the boom and withdraw the load into the safe envelope.

A system was designed to perform in this manner and is fitted to every vehicle. The essential feature is that the manual lever-operated valves, which control the two motions described, automatically centralise when the danger zone is approached, overriding the operator's input. Two considerations of the above, *vis à vis* the designer and potential hazards, now spring to mind. The first (and this is a true story) relates to such a vehicle operating with an Irish company. An official complaint was lodged with the manufacturer that the levers fitted to the control valves were not strong enough and indeed some had broken.

Subsequent investigation revealed that when the safety system had come into operation with valves centralising, lights flashing and buzzers sounding, the operator had attempted to extend the load range by application of pipes to the levers. Naturally, long pieces of pipe and tremendous effort were required to overcome the system even partially, the net result being the bending and ultimate fracture of the levers, hence the request for stronger levers.

Figure 15 *Giraffe site placement vehicle*

Matbro-Bray

If an accident had resulted from this practice, under which defect classification would the above be considered?

— a defect of specification: should it have been foreseen at the outset that operators would attempt to override the safety system by the application of pipes to the valve levers?

— a defect of design: if the control levers had snapped, injuring the operator, should they have been made strong enough to accept pipes of infinite length?

— a defect of manufacture: was the lever material not to specification?

A vehicle of similar design has since appeared on the market with a safety system which sounds a klaxon and flashes a light in the event of movement of the load outside the safe envelope of operation. If these are ignored the danger zone can be entered and instability may result. Should an accident occur with this vehicle, it is interesting to speculate whether it would be considered a defect of design or specification. As the Giraffe pre-empted this latter system, would it give rise to questions in the area of 'reasonable user expectation'?

See Case History 16.

## SOURCE

Pugh, S (1979) Give the designer a chance. *Product Liability International*. Colchester, Lloyd's of London Press Limited.

# CASE HISTORY 10

## Electric Cabling

One way of managing product risk is to identify a particular hazard, define the means by which it could occur and then establish a programme to avoid or reduce it. Fault Tree Analysis, see Chapter 7 and Case History 1, uses the system in the form of a logic diagram, working from the undesired event back down to individual components. Failure Mode Effects Analysis, see Chapter 7, starts with the individual components and works up to the undesired event, and can complement a FTA.

A practical example of this approach to design is found in Raychem's study of the behaviour of cable insulation materials in fire situations. Their particular interest is in the use of cables for military purposes and the development of low fire hazard materials for the jacketing of complex cables, for application in the Royal Navy and off-shore installations. The rapid spread of electronic devices in domestic and industrial areas also makes the use of fire resistant cables of wider importance. Most modern cables are insulated with jackets based on natural polymers (eg rubber) or synthetic polymers (eg polyethylene (PE) or polyvinyl chloride (PVC)). Being organic polymers these insulation materials can burn and thus contribute very significantly to the overall fireload in any given environment.

When a polymer on a cable core is exposed to a fire a complicated chain of chemical events is initiated. If the polymer has a relatively low melting point, it could begin to melt and drip when first exposed to the heat of the fire.

As the temperature rises the ignition temperature of the polymer will eventually be reached and burning will commence. Drips of burning polymer could fall from the cable and, if they do not self-extinguish immediately, they could fall on to other ignitable material and start another fire.

If there is insufficient oxygen available, or it is not hot enough to cause complete combustion of the organic polymer, the off gases will be heavily contaminated with unburnt carbon particles, thus forming a dense smoke. The flames of the burning polymer could propagate rapidly along the cable length, due to the potential flammability of the polymer and the conduction of heat along the copper core of the cable. The off gases from the burning of certain polymers can contain significant quantities of gases that could cause corrosion damage to other equipment or structures, or be hazardous to human beings by causing irritation, inflammation or malfunction of soft tissues in the eyes, nose and lungs.

To lower the overall fire hazard each of these interelated events had to be studied separately and action taken to reduce the risk it presented. At the same time critical mechanical and electrical properties had to be retained for the material to function as a high quality cable jacket. To test a specially developed new material five parameters were taken:

1   Ease of ignition. A sample of the polymer is ignited and allowed to burn in an atmosphere of oxygen and nitrogen in which the concentration of oxygen can be varied. Determining the percentage concentration of oxygen that is required to allow the polymer *just* to continue burning, gives a measure of the relative ignitability of specimens of different polymeric formulations. The higher the amount of oxygen required the harder the polymer is to ignite.

2   Flame propagation. An alternative way to conduct the above test is to keep the oxygen content constant at 21 per cent (as in the normal atmosphere), and raise the temperature of the oxygen/nitrogen mixture to find the temperature above which the polymer continues to burn once ignited.

Comparison of the temperature required for continued combustion for different materials provides an indication of the relative ease of flame propagation by a given material. The higher the temperature, the more difficult it is for the flame to propagate in a fire.

3   Smoke generation. Smoke consists of a suspension of fine particles which obscures vision. The hazard associated with dense smoke is that it makes it extremely difficult for victims trapped in a fire to find their way to an exit, and equally it makes it difficult

for members of the rescue services to locate victims in a fire-enveloped area. Most tests for comparison of smoke generated from burning polymers rely on some optical method for measuring the degree of obscuration of a light path caused by the smoke. One particular example is NES 711, which is a test designed by the British Naval Engineering Division, in which a low smoke index indicates better visibility.

(4)  Corrosivity of off gases. The major part of the corrosion caused by off gases from burning polymers is due to the acidic gases. The standard type of test seeks to measure the total amount of acid gas by absorption into a solution of alkali. Polymers containing chlorine or bromine generate hydrogen chloride and hydrogen bromide, respectively.

These acids can arise from the polymer (eg PVC), or some of the conventional additives used to treat polymers to make them less flammable. The new material specifically avoided additives or polymers that could generate these acids, because they are particularly corrosive and also hazardous to humans.

(5)  Hazard rating for humans. For general testing purposes it is not practicable to undertake true biological testing. The approach used is to carry out a straightforward chemical analysis for gases generally considered to be hazardous (eg acid gases, hydrogen cyanide, carbon monoxide, etc) and then use some agreed formula to compute a hazard rating from the measured concentrations.

Using these five parameters the new material was found to be superior to rubber, polyethylene or polyvinyl chloride and to present a lower fire hazard.

## SOURCE

Raychem Limited.

# CASE HISTORY 11

## Leyland Roadrunner

The commercial vehicle is a product where user safety can only be introduced by design. The engineer is encouraged to adopt the view that engineering and design are the creative forces behind vehicle safety, and that much of the content of a good design is the thought and effort directed to producing a safe design.

The specification of the Roadrunner is for a 6 to 10 tonne vehicle, with the 7.5 tonne model sold in considerable numbers as a popular vehicle for delivery work in town centres. For this type of application the Roadrunner needs to be manoeuverable with good all-round vision for the driver; he must be able to move the vehicle in confined spaces, such as shopping precincts, without risk to bystanders and pedestrians. The 'kerb-side' window has been designed with this safety requirement in mind. It enables the driver to see the critical area, by the kerb-side, which would otherwise remain a blind spot.

The Roadrunner cab interior has been designed on an ergonomic basis, so that the optimum layout and positioning of the controls, instruments, windows and mirrors has been achieved, with consequent safety benefits. This design process has been carried out using a computer-aided design package, which allows the designer to 'view' the driver environments from a number of different angles within the cab, for various driver positions. It was on this basis that the value of the kerb-side window was decided, and also on its exact location and size.

The Roadrunner windscreen is a technological innovation, with improved safety features. First, it has a laminated screen, safer than toughened glass. Accident research has shown that the primary need in a collision is to retain the occupants within the passenger compartment, and this is better achieved with laminated glass. Second, the screen is directly glazed into the cab shell, contributing to the strength and stability of the cab

Figure 16 *Kerb-side safety window on the Leyland Road Runner*

system. The windscreen provides much improved visibility over conventional vehicles of this type and size.

The Roadrunner won a Design Council award in 1986.

**SOURCE**

Leyland Vehicles.

# CASE HISTORY 12

## Safe Operation of Pig Launcher/Receivers

The potential for human error in the operation of process plant is enormous. In the petrochemical industry in particular, where high volumes of flammable or volatile fluids are often piped under pressure and at elevated temperatures, the consequences of an incorrectly opened valve can prove catastrophic. Fortunately, experience and common sense have resulted in extensive safety legislation to protect workers and the public from death or injury, and plant from accidental or malicious damage. One direct result has been an international acceptance of interlocking as the most reliable means of eliminating human error from manual plant operation.

Interlocking has developed on the principle that actions performed in the correct sequence are safe, but are potentially lethal or damaging if the incorrect sequence is followed. Once an interlock system has been fitted, the equipment is made safe because it can only be operated in a correctly predetermined and interdependent sequence. The operator is inexorably led step by step through the operation with no possibility of deviation.

A typical example of the application of a safety interlock system to a formerly hazardous operation is on a pig launcher/receiver. In the chemical processing and petrochemical industries, pipelines carrying gases or liquids frequently need cleaning, purging or surveying. This is usually carried out by an operation known as pigging.

A plug or 'pig', which may be more than 2m long and 1m in diameter, is inserted into the pipeline. The product carried in the pipeline is fed behind the pig under operating line pressure to project it along the pipe run. To insert and retrieve the pig requires direct access to the pipeline by means of a close circuit piping loop at each end of the pipe run.

Accidental opening of access hatches can be extremely dangerous on gas lines, which may have an operating line pressure as high as 20 psi, or may result in considerable product

Figure 17 *Method of safely cleaning a pressurised pipeline using a special 'pig'*

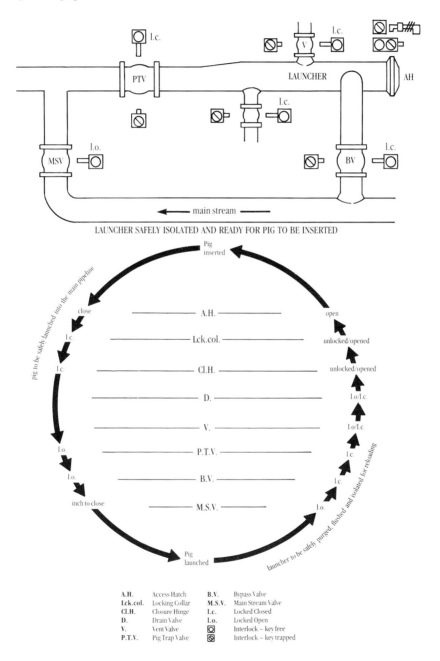

spillage on large bore liquid pipelines. It is therefore essential that access hatches at the launch and receive points are positively locked shut while the system is pressurised, and remain locked until the launch and receive loops are isolated at atmospheric pressure.

Safe isolation of the piping loops can be achieved only by operating the associated valves in a single correct sequence. Installation of a safety interlock system not only imposes this correct sequence on an operator, but also makes correct operation a pre-requisite for opening the access hatch. Conversely, the launch and receive loops cannot be pressurised until the hatches are closed and locked.

A safety interlock system specifically for pig launcher/receivers was first developed in 1981 by Castell, who had supplied interlocks for a pressure safety valve system on the then new Danbor Gorm E production platform. They were asked by Danbor to design a similar system to ensure rapid and safe operation of the platform's pig launcher/receivers. Until then, similar installations had been either padlocked, controlled by permit to work, or subject to operator supervision.

The method of interlocking ensured complete safety in the pigging operation and has since become standard practice within the petrochemical industry. Although many safety interlock systems have been successfully retrofitted to existing pig launcher/receivers, the strength of current safety legislation pertaining to off shore petrochemical operations is pointing system consultants and designers towards specifying tailored interlock systems at the conceptual design stage of off-shore projects.

## SOURCE

Castell Safety International Limited.

# CASE HISTORY 13

## *Crow v. Barford (Agricultural) Limited and HB Holttum & Company Limited*
### Court of Appeal 8 April 1963

This is an important United Kingdom landmark case for designers as it turned on the foreseeability of risk, and the designer's potential liability for defective design.

In his judgment Lord Justice Diplock said

The plaintiff, who is a farmer, purchased in 1958 a machine known as a new Barford 18-inch Rotomo, which was a rotary grass cutter. He purchased the machine from the second defendants, who were dealers in and retailers of machinery of that kind, describing themselves as light tractor specialists. The machine was manufactured by the first defendants, Barford (Agricultural) Limited. It was of the ordinary design of a rotary grass cutter with revolving blades which were covered by an iron case or shield, and it was operated by a Villiers two-stroke motor. The motor ran the blades; the machine itself was pushed and not power-driven in that sense. The guard for the blades had an aperture for expelling the grass as it was cut, which was on the right-hand side of the machine. The engine, which was on top of the machine, had a recoil starter handle, which had to be pulled in order to start the engine. The recoil starter handle was also on the right-hand side of the machine, and the normal way of starting the motor was to put one's left hand upon the handle of the machine, one's right hand on the starter, and one's right foot on the iron casing to the side and to the rear of the aperture.

Mr Crow bought this machine after considering various other machines of different makes, and after a demonstration when Mr Holttum, employed by the second defendants, brought it to his farm and showed him how it worked.

At that demonstration Mr Crow inspected the machine, and in particular inspected the knives; and it must

145

have been evident on any such inspection not only what the aperture was for, but also what was plain for everyone to see, where the starter handle was, that the knives revolved within one-eighth of an inch or so of the opening of the aperture, and that it would obviously be very dangerous if a foot or a hand or any part of the human body got into the aperture while the knives were revolving.

The machine was delivered in December 1958, and towards Easter 1959, when the grass began to grow, Mr Crow desired to use it for cutting his grass. He used it on one or two occasions prior to the accident, and on those occasions it started easily enough. But on Easter Saturday (which was 28 March 1959) it did not start when he wished to start it. He had it at that time on some concrete in the yard on his farm, I think. He discovered by examining it that there was an air lock in the petrol feed, and, having cured that, he tried again to start it. It was difficult to start, and he had to pull the handle of the recoil starter a number of times, doing it in the way in which he had been shown to do it by Mr Holttum, by holding the handle of the machine with his left hand, grasping the starter with his right hand, and with his right foot on the casing by the side of the aperture towards the rear of the machine. Unfortunately, the last time that he pulled the starting handle, the engine started, and in some way which he was unable to explain, his right foot slipped, it went into the aperture, and as a result two of his toes were cut off, a most unfortunate accident.

He brings this action against the manufacturers and the retailers of the machine, against the manufacturers for negligence and breach of duty in 'manufacturing and distributing without giving any warning of its true nature an article, namely, the mower which was dangerous in itself, or alternatively in failing to take reasonable care in the design or manufacture of the mower to prevent the purchaser and user thereof, namely, the plaintiff, being exposed to the danger of his foot being caught by the blades on starting up the same.'

He sued the second defendants, the retailers, for breach of the implied warranty of merchantable quality contained in the Sale of Goods Act 1893, Section 14 (2).

I deal first with the claim against the manufacturers, for that was put upon the grounds of the decision in Donoghue v Stevenson (1932) AC 562, on the duty of a manufacturer to use reasonable care in the preparation and putting up of goods which he puts upon the market and which he knows are 'likely to reach the ultimate consumer in the form in which they left him with no reasonable possibility of intermediate examination, and with the knowledge that the absence of reasonable care in the preparation or putting up of the product will result in an injury to the consumer's life or property'. The principle in Donoghue v Stevenson which lays that duty upon a manufacturer is subject to this limitation set out in the case of Grant v Australian Knitting Mills [1936] AC 85, that the principle can be applied only where the defect is hidden and unknown to the customer or consumer; that is set out in the headnote and is in fact a quotation from page 120 of the opinion of their Lordships in that Privy Council case. The requirement is dichotomous: the defect must be hidden as well as unknown to the consumer.

I pause, therefore, to ask: What is the defect which there is said to be in this machine? The answer seems to be that the aperture and the starter handle were on the same side of the machine; that in order to start it, it was proper (though it may not have been necessary) to put your right foot on the casing not far from the aperture, and that so to do involved a danger that your foot might slip and get into the aperture. That defect, or at any rate the physical design of the machine, was in no sense hidden. It was perfectly obvious on looking at the machine that there was the aperture as large as life, there were the knives, and there was the starting handle. It was quite obvious that if you were going to use the machine and start the blades revolving, it would be very dangerous indeed to allow your foot or any part of your body to get in the aperture.

So that so far as the physical design of the machine is concerned, and in so far as that design was a defect of the machine, in no sense can it be said to be hidden. *Prima facie*, therefore, it is a defect to which the rule in Donoghue v Stevenson does not apply.

Mr Martin Jukes has sought to put it in this way. He says that the physical design of the machine which is obvious is not the defect. What is the defect is the danger that someone's foot might slip when starting the machine in the usual way for starting it. I think that is a misuse of the word 'defect' in the Donoghue v Stevenson rule. But assuming, if one may, that a danger of that kind which was a consequence of the design could be a 'defect' within the Donoghue v Stevenson rule, it could be so only if two conditions were fulfilled: (1) that the manufacturer should foresee the risk of danger to the user; that it should be reasonably foreseeable; and (2) — for this is the meaning of the expression that the defect must be hidden — that the user of the machine could not reasonably foresee the risk.

As I put to Mr Jukes in the course of his argument, it seems to me that the plaintiff in this case is in a dilemma. Either the risk of the foot slipping in the circumstances in which it did slip in the unfortunate case of Mr Crow was not reasonably foreseeable, or it was. The learned judge, who saw the machine and the demonstration and heard the witnesses, expressed the view at the end of his judgment: 'I do not think that in the early part of 1959 the first defendants could reasonably have foreseen the likelihood of an accident such as the plaintiff sustained, or indeed that there was any foreseeable risk of danger. In my judgment it is really going altogether too far to suggest that a manufacturer fails in his duty to the public if, in the early days of manufacture of a machine of this sort, he fails to anticipate that an operator might be wearing wellington boots; he might slip or over-balance; he might pull the machine in such a way that his foot in a wellington boot would get into the aperture.'

If the learned judge is right (and that seems very much a matter for the trial judge) then the risk was not a foreseeable risk and there was no lack of care on the part of the manufacturers in marketing a machine of this kind.

The alternative horn of the dilemma — assuming that the learned judge was wrong, and that this risk was a foreseeable one — is that it is a risk (whatever view you take of the likelihood of its occurrence) which is perfectly apparent when you look at the machine in order to form a judgment as to its likelihood or otherwise. The possibility of its happening, and the way in which it could happen, is perfectly obvious, and as obvious to the plaintiff and to Mr

Holttum and the retailer as it was to the manufacturer. Therefore, if it was a risk sufficiently likely to be foreseeable, it could not amount to a hidden defect so as to place on the manufacturer the duty to avoid marketing a machine in which that risk was present. So far as the action against the manufacturers is concerened, it appears to me that this appeal must fail.

As regards the action against the retailers, which was based upon the implied condition of merchantable quality contained in the Sale of Goods Act 1893, I should perhaps read it from Section 14 (2): 'Where goods are bought by description from a seller who deals in goods of that description (whether he be the manufacturer or not)' — that was the case of the second defendants — 'there is an implied condition that the goods shall be of merchantable quality; provided that if the buyer has examined the goods, there shall be no implied condition as regards defects which such examination ought to have revealed'. What I have said in relation to the liability of the manufacturer would involve that the proviso applies in this case if it were right to say (which I do not accept) that this machine was not of merchantable quality.

Appeal dismissed with costs.

## SOURCE

Ashworth, J S (ed) (1984) *Product Liability Casebook*. Colchester, Lloyd's of London Press Limited.

# CASE HISTORY 14

## Wormell v. *RHM Agricultural (East) Ltd*
Court of Appeal 6 December 1985

For the purposes of Section 14 of the Sale of Goods Act 1979, the word 'goods' included the packaging and instructions for the goods, so that goods and instructions which were misleading were not reasonably fit for their purpose and further, although the instructions were provided by the manufacturers, the retailer of the goods was liable under Section 14 for breach of the implied term that the goods were fit for their purpose.

The plaintiff was an experienced farmer who had sowed 800 acres of winter wheat in 1982. The wet and cold spring prevented farmers getting on to their land to spray herbicides and by March 1983 Mr Wormell had not been able to use any wild oats killer, even though he wanted to do so. The defendants told him that 'Commando' was the only one to use; it was understood that it would be used in accordance with the instructions. The plaintiff was not able to get on to his land until June. Before spraying he read the instructions on the can carefully. The spray had only a limited effect but because of the wet ground 'Commando' could not have been used effectively at all in 1983. This was known only to Shell and other experts in the field; all that was known to the plaintiff, and other farmers, was what appeared on the can. The label covered virtually the whole of the can and contained detailed information and instructions. Two questions arose. First, how did the plaintiff understand the instructions, and second, how would a reasonable user understand them?

There was no doubt that the plaintiff understood the label as meaning, provided there were good growing conditions, he could kill wild oats whatever time he sprayed but if he sprayed beyond the recommended time, there was a risk to his crop.

On a fair reading of the instructions, they did represent that it was dangerous to spray the crop outside the recommended period, but provided it was sprayed during good growing conditions, wild oats would be killed.

The plaintiff's understanding of the instructions was that which any reasonable user would receive from them. There was not any statement that if 'Commando' was applied later than the suggested time, then that would reduce the activity of 'Commando' against wild oats. Yet that was something which Shell had ample evidence of.

The plaintiff's claim was solely in contract for breach of terms implied by Section 14 (2) and (3) of the Sale of Goods Act 1979. On the evidence, 'Commando' was an effective wild oats killer provided that it was applied at specific times.

The plaintiff's case was that the 'Commando' was not reasonably fit for use as wild oats killer if it was applied in accordance with a fair interpretation of the instructions.

The instructions were not a term of the contract. They were not representations made either by the defendants or by Shell. However the word 'goods' could be construed to mean the herbicide 'Commando' or the herbicide 'Commando' in its container with its packing and instructions.

No one would sell such a chemical without detailed instructions for its use. If it was sold without any instructions it would be totally unmerchantable.

The user had to know how to use it and where to use it. On the former construction, it would not be of merchantable quality because the user would not know how to use it.

The only reasonable meaning of 'goods' included the packing and instructions. The goods must be looked at as a whole to see if they were of merchantable quality or reasonably fit for their purpose.

Although the user was relying on instructions provided by the manufacturer, nevertheless the retailer was warranting that the goods, used in accordance with instructions, would be reasonably fit for their purpose.

If there were no instructions as to when a chemical could be applied, it could not be reasonably fit for its purpose if it was only fit for its purpose at certain specified times.

In considering whether 'Commando' was reasonably fit for its purpose, the instructions or warnings on the container could properly be taken into account.

Those instructions were misleading. They were not clear. If a retailer sold goods, for example, a chemical with its container and instructions, and the instructions made the goods not fit for their purpose, then there was a breach of Section 14 and a breach by the retailer or seller even if he had not the technical knowledge to see if the instructions were accurate.

The breach did not cause damage to the plaintiff's crop but caused him to waste his money, in particular to waste his 'Commando' and the money involved in spraying it and he was entitled to be compensated for those costs.[*]

## SOURCE

*The Times* 27 December 1985.

[*] This decision was overturned on appeal. It was held that the instructions in this particular case were not misleading, but the principle of instructions being part of goods remains undisturbed.

# CASE HISTORY 15

## *Greenman* v. *Yuba Power Products Inc*

### Supreme Court of California 24 January 1963

This United States landmark case is frequently quoted in connection with strict liability. Justice Traynor in his judgment said, 'A manufacturer is strictly liable in tort when an article he places on the market, knowing that it is to be used without inspection for defects, proves to have a defect that causes injury to human beings.'

The plaintiff brought an action for damages against the retailer and the manufacturer of a Shopsmith, a combination power tool that could be used as a saw, drill and wood lathe. He saw a Shopsmith demonstrated by the retailer and studied a brochure prepared by the manufacturer. He decided he wanted a Shopsmith for his home workshop, and his wife bought and gave him one for Christmas in 1955. In 1957 he bought the necessary attachments to use the Shopsmith as a lathe for turning a large piece of wood he wished to make into a chalice. After he had worked on the piece of wood several times without difficulty, it suddenly flew out of the machine and struck him on the forehead, inflicting serious injuries. About ten and half months later, he gave the retailer and the manufacturer written notice of claimed breaches of warranties and filed a complaint against them alleging such breaches and negligence.

The manufacturer's brochure included the following statements:

1  When Shopsmith is in horizontal position — Rugged construction of frame provides rigid support from end to end. Heavy centerless-ground steel tubing insures perfect alignment of components.
2  Shopsmith maintains its accuracy because every component has positive locks that hold adjustments through rough or precision work.

Our interest in this case concerns the design element and the jury heard substantial evidence to show that it was defective.

Witnesses testified that inadequate set screws were used to hold parts of the machine together, so that normal vibration caused the tailstock of the lathe to move away from the piece of wood being turned, permitting it to fly out of the lathe. They also testified that there were other more positive ways of fastening the parts of the machine together, the use of which would have prevented the accident.

In concluding his judgment Justice Traynor said, 'To establish the manufacturer's liability it was sufficient that plaintiff proved that he was injured while using the Shopsmith in a way it was intended to be used as a result of a defect in design and manufacture of which plaintiff was not aware that made the Shopsmith unsafe for its intended use.'

The trial court had returned a verdict for the retailer against the plaintiff and for the plaintiff against the manufacturer in the amount of $65 000. The judgment was affirmed.

## SOURCE

Ashworth, J S (ed) (1984) *Product Liability Casebook*. Colchester, Lloyd's of London Press Limited.

# CASE HISTORY 16

## *Barker* v. *Lull Engineering Company Inc*
### Supreme Court of California 16 January 1978

Fifteen years had elapsed since *Greenman* (Case History 15) and during that period the courts in the United States had on many occasions established that the law recognised strict liability for defective products. What it had not been able to establish was what was meant by 'defective'.

In *Barker*, the jury instruction was, 'I instruct you that strict liability for the defect in design of a product is based on a finding that the product was unreasonably dangerous for its intended use, and in turn the unreasonableness of the danger must necessarily be derived from the state of the art at the time of the design. The manufacturer or lessor are not insurers of their products. However, an industry cannot set its own standards.'

In judgment Acting Chief Justice Tobriner said

Plaintiff Barker sustained serious injuries as a result of an accident which occurred while he was operating a Lull High-Lift Loader at a construction site. The loader, manufactured in 1967, is a piece of heavy construction equipment designed to lift loads of up to 5000 pounds to a maximum height of 32ft. The loader is 23ft long, 8ft wide and weighs 17 050 pounds; it sits on four large rubber tyres which are about the height of a person's chest, and is equipped with four-wheel drive, an automatic transmission with no park position and a hand brake. Loads are lifted by forks similar to the forks of a forklift.

The loader is designed so that the load can be kept level even when the loader is being operated on sloping terrain. The levelling of the load is controlled by a lever located near the steering column, and positioned between the operator's legs. The lever is equipped with a manual lock that can be engaged to prevent accidental slipping of the load level during lifting.

The loader was not equipped with seat belts or a roll bar. A wire and pipe cage over the driver's seat afforded the driver some protection from falling objects. The cab of the loader was located at least nine feet behind the lifting forks.

On the day of the accident the regular operator of the loader, Bill Dalton, did not report for work, and plaintiff, who had received only limited instruction on the operation of the loader from Dalton and who had operated the loader on only a few occasions, was assigned to run the loader in Dalton's place. The accident occurred while plaintiff was attempting to lift a load of lumber to a height of approximately 18 to 20ft and to place the load on the second storey of a building under construction. The lift was a particularly difficult one because the terrain on which the loader rested sloped sharply in several directions.

Witnesses testified that plaintiff approached the structure with the loader, levelled the forks to compensate for the sloping ground and lifted the load to a height variously estimated between 10 and 18ft. During the course of the lift plaintiff felt some vibration, and, when it appeared to several co-workers that the load was beginning to tip, the workers shouted to plaintiff to jump from the loader. Plaintiff heeded these warnings and leaped from the loader, but while scrambling away he was struck by a piece of falling lumber and suffered serious injury.

Although the above facts were generally not in dispute, the parties differed markedly in identifying the responsible causes for the accident. Plaintiff contended *inter alia* that the accident was attributable to one or more design defects of the loader. Defendant, in turn, denied that the loader was defective in any respect, and claimed that the accident resulted either from plaintiff's lack of skill or from his misuse of its product.

The court reviewed the meaning of defect and concluded that a product is defective in design either (1) if the product has failed to perform as safely as an ordinary consumer would expect when used in an intended or reasonably foreseeable manner, or (2) if, in light of the relevant factors discussed below, the benefits of the challenged design outweigh the risk of danger inherent in such design. In addition, the allocation of the burden of proof with respect to the latter 'risk benefit' standard is explained.

This dual standard for design defect assures an injured plaintiff protection from products that either fall below ordinary consumer expectations as to safety, or that, on balance, are not as safely designed as they should be. At the same time, the standard permits a manufacturer who has marketed a product which satisfies ordinary consumer expectations to demonstrate the relative complexity of design decisions and the trade-offs that are frequently required in the adoption of alternative designs.

Finally, this test reflects our continued adherence to the principle that, in a product liability action, the trier of fact must focus on the product, not on the manufacturer's conduct, and that the plaintiff need not prove that the manufacturer acted unreasonably or negligently in order to prevail in such an action.

The judgment previously given in favour of the defendants was reversed. (See Case History 9.)

## SOURCE

Ashworth, J S (ed) (1984) *Product Liability Casebook*. Colchester, Lloyd's of London Press Limited.

# CASE HISTORY 17

## *Larsen* v. *General Motors Corporation*
### United States Court of Appeals,
### Eighth Circuit 1968

This is a design case which emphasises the difficulty of establishing liability in design cases without using the language of negligence, even when the action is based on strict liability. The issue was whether the duty of an automobile manufacturer extended to persons injured in a collision that was not caused by any defect in the vehicle.

In 1964 Erling David Larsen received severe bodily injuries while driving a Chevrolet Corvair which was in a head-on collision. The impact occurred on the left front corner of the Corvair causing a severe rearward thrust to the steering mechanism into the plaintiff's head. The plaintiff did not contend that the design caused the accident, but that because of the design he received injuries he would not otherwise have received or, his injuries would not have been as severe. The rearward displacement of the steering shaft on impact was much greater on the Corvair than it would have been in other cars, that were designed to protect against such displacement.

General Motors contended that it 'has no duty whatsoever to design and manufacture a vehicle... which is otherwise "safe" or "safer" to occupy during collision impacts'. Since there is no duty there can be no actionable negligence on its part to either design a safe or more safe car, or to warn of any inherent or latent defects in design that might make its cars less safe than some other cars manufactured, either by it or other manufacturers.

This is a 'second collision' case and it had been held before Larsen that a collision was not an intended use, and therefore the manufacturer had no duty to an injured person. However, the reasoning later adopted by the courts, in Larsen and in subsequent cases, is that the test of liability is not 'intended use' but 'foreseeable use'. Collisions can be foreseen and manufacturers have a duty to reduce as much as they can the consequences of a collision.

In a later case the court said, 'Since collisions for whatever cause are foreseeable events, the scope of liability should be commensurate with the scope of the foreseeable risk.' Collisions are the natural consequences of the intended use of automobile. This reasoning has now almost universally been adopted in the United States.

In the Larsen case the Circuit Judge ended his judgment with:

> If, because of the alleged undisclosed defect in design of the 1963 Corvair steering assembly, an extra hazard is created over and above the normal hazard, General Motors should be liable for this unreasonable hazard. Admittedly, it would not sell many cars of this particular model if its sales pitch included the cautionary statement that the user is subjected to an extra hazard or unreasonable risk in the event of a head-on collision. But the duty of reasonable care should command a warning of this latent defect that could under certain circumstances accentuate the possibility of severe injury.... For the reasons set forth, we reverse and remand for proceedings not inconsistent with this opinion.

## SOURCE

Ashworth, J S (ed) (1984) *Product Liability Casebook*. Colchester, Lloyd's of London Press Limited.

# CASE HISTORY 18

## *LeBouef* v. *The Goodyear Tire & Rubber Company*
### United States Court of Appeals Fifth Circuit 1980

Goodyear's liability was based upon a defective design, although there was in fact nothing wrong with its tyre except that it was not suitable for speeds above 85 miles per hour. The defect was the failure to warn of this limitation as instructions and warnings form a significant part of a design. The relevant wording in connection with the LeBouef case is, 'In order to prevent the product from being unreasonably dangerous, the seller may be required to give directions or warnings, on the container, as to its use.'

In 1976 Shelby Leleux bought a new Mercury Cougar car fitted with Goodyear HR78-15 Custom Polysteel Radial Tyres. The tyres were standard equipment for the Cougar, despite the fact that they had actually been designed and tested by Goodyear only for a maximum safe operating speed of around 85 miles per hour. About 10 per cent of the tyres of this type that Goodyear had subjected to speed tests, of 95 to 100 miles per hour for thirty minute periods, did not survive the test. The Cougar was designed with a capability of more than 100 miles per hour.

Despite the disparity in the design capabilities, and at least Ford's knowledge of this, the only 'warning' associated with the use of the tyres at high speeds provided by either party, aside from inflation instructions, was a statement in the Cougar owner's manual that 'continuous driving over 90 miles per hour requires using high-speed-capability tires'.

The manual did not state whether the tyres in question were or were not of high speed calibre.

At about 5.00 am on the morning of 6 June 1976 Leleux and his friend Floyd Dugas, both of whom had been drinking since 9.00 pm on the previous evening, were travelling in the Cougar at over a hundred miles an hour when the tread separated from the carcass of the left rear tyre, which caused an accident in which Leleux was killed and Dugas seriously injured. A blood alcohol test revealed that Leleux's blood contained levels of alcohol well above established standards for intoxication. The separation of the tread from the left rear tyre was found later not to have been caused by road hazards or neglected cuts in the tread.

The case was tried under Louisiana law, which is based on the civil law of France, and the courts in the State think of liability in terms of the violation of a duty, in this case the duty of the manufacturer to warn. The defendants were found to be liable for selling a product that was defective, the defect being the absence of a warning. At the time of the accident the driver was intoxicated, and although at first sight it would seem that a warning would have been disregarded in any case, and that the real cause of the accident was drunken driving, the Court did not take that view. The tyre was defective because there was no warning and contributory negligence was no defence.

Assumption of risk is a defence in a product liability claim, and an attempt was made to argue that the passenger could not recover because he had voluntarily assumed the risk of accompanying a drunken driver. Since, however, the drunkenness was held not to be a cause of the accident that argument did not succeed.

The Court of Appeals upheld the judgment of the District Court and its judgment in favour of the plaintiff was affirmed. The case is authority for the statement that, at least in Louisiana, the expression 'normal use' includes 'foreseeable use'. This is in line with the decisions on second collisions in which it has been held that the manufacturer of motor cars should foresee the possibilities of accidents.

## SOURCE

Ashworth, J S (ed) (1984) *Product Liability Casebook*. Colchester, Lloyd's of London Press Limited.

# CASE HISTORY 19

## *Richard Winward* v. *TVR Engineering Limited*
### Court of Appeal 4 March 1986

TVR Engineering manufactured a car in 1973; when it caught fire in 1981 Mrs Winward was involved. The appeal was against the judgment of Her Honour Judge Mary Holt who had held the defendants liable in negligence and that the plaintiff could recover damages.

TVR's Managing Director, Mr Halstead, who had not held that office in 1973, explained the role of his company in purchasing components and incorporating them into their cars. He described the warranty that the firm used to get from Ford thus, 'We tend to ride on the back of Ford and go along with what they recommend... on matters of engineering we would be led by Ford Motor Company and use the parts which were recommended by them. We buy original equipment. Once led by people like Ford we cast an engineering eye over their equipment and if we are in agreement we use it.' TVR submitted that this was a reasonable standard of prudence and practice which discharged any legal obligation of reasonable care which lay upon them.

It was common ground that the fire which gave rise to the claim was ignited at, or directly proximate to the carburettor, which had partly melted.

The first explanation, proffered on behalf of the plaintiff, was accepted by the learned judge who had said

> In my judgement one salient fact emerges namely that it was not good engineering practice, even though a commonly used commercial practice, to employ a push fit between metals having a different co-efficient of expansion. Mr Dias (an expert witness for the plaintiff) considered it a retrograde and risky practice and I accept his view of the matter. In the case of the ferrule in the Weber carburettor the push fit was used for a brass ferrule and a zinc alloy cased carburettor with a difference of 200° [*sic*] in rates of expansion. Moreover, I also accept Mr Dias' view

that all push fits involve a manufacture to tolerance levels and that any movement of the ferrule will loosen the fit. Mr Makinson (an expert witness for the defendants) accepted that to be 100 per cent sure of avoiding risk a locking device was required.

Given the fact that in service it could be expected that the fuel inlet pipes would be replaced and with a bevelled edge to the ferrule and the normal hardening of the pipes could be expected to be used to detach the pipes it appears to me to be clearly foreseeable that the ferrule would become loosened with the consequent risk of its becoming detached and a fire resulting.

In my opinion (the defendants) manufactured a car in 1973 which was defective in design and which carried within its carburettor a push fit ferrule the retention force of which was likely to be diminished because of the differential expansion of the respective metals of the ferrule and casing of the carburettor and that it was a foreseeable risk that during servicing the ferrule might be loosened by twisting with the further risk of fire from detachment.

In my judgment (the defendants) were negligent in failing to examine or make tests on the Weber carburettors which they used in their engines and in failing to modify the ferrule by inserting into it a locking or screwing device to prevent the risk of detachment and in failing to warn owners of the relevant cars of the existence of the resultant danger.

In the Court of Appeal Sir Roualeyn Cumming-Bruce summed up this first explanation by saying it concerned, 'an inherent design fault in the fit of the brass ferrule which accounted for the eventual displacement of the ferrule after gradually [*sic*] over the years it had become loose in its seating so as to be subject to displacement upon the application, at the end of the day, of whatever fault it was which brought about the final unseating of the ferrule.' In a word: it was the unseating of the ferrule that caused the fire.

The second explanation, put forward by TVR, took the opposite view saying that the ferrule became unseated as a consequence of the fire, and was not a cause of the fire. The second explanation was summarised as it, 'being due to a defect in a pin within the chamber of a carburettor which, in the ways described in the defendants' expert's report, produced ignition within the chamber of the carburettor such that the heat thereby produced caused the carburettor to melt and come apart...'.

The expert witness, Mr Makinson, had said that Ford and Reliant had used thousands of these carburettors.

> There was nothing in his experience to lead him to the inference that, in spite of the use of this carburettor with this kind of brass ferrule push fit for at least a dozen years in thousands of cars, there was any reason until this occasion, if at all, for suspecting the seating of the ferrule had ever caused any trouble at all, much less a fire, whereas there was some concensus of engineering opinion that other fires that had arisen when this carburettor was used could be traced to a quite different cause. Looking at all the possibilities, Makinson explained his reasons for thinking that the ferrule came out on this occasion as a consequence of the fire and not as a contributing cause.

Sir Roualeyn Cumming-Bruce agreed with the first explanation saying

> There was ample evidence on which the judge was entitled to conclude that, without postulating any esoteric engineering expertise, any manufacturer applying his mind to basic engineering principles should have appreciated that it was not good engineering practice to employ a push fit instead of a screw fit between two metals having a different co-efficient of expansion. The judge was entitled to accept Mr Dias' opinion that such a practice was a retrograde and risky one, and accept it the learned judge did.

A quite separate proposition, on which TVR relied, was that there was no reasonably foreseeable risk which imposed upon them any obligation either to minimise the risk, by taking such action as introducing a pin, or to warn the users of manufactured vehicles.

Sir Roualeyn Cumming-Bruce said

> These manufacturers were not insurers. Their duty of care was limited to take reasonable care for the safety of the consumer who drove the car. The duty of care, of course,

varies with the particular facts and Lord Justice Asquith (as he then was) neatly expressed the equation when he contrasted the magnitude of the risk with the gravity of the consequences if risk supervened. The appellant's case here is that, on the history disclosed before the judge, the defendants, when purchasing and incorporating in their motorcar a Ford engine with a Weber carburettor, were entitled to take the view which they did that there was absolutely nothing in the history of this carburettor to put the defendants on enquiry before incorporating a carburettor and a Ford engine in a motorcar which they had designed and proceeded to assemble.

The learned judge had disagreed because she accepted that it was simply not good engineering practice to rely on the push fit. Mr Makinson, giving evidence on behalf of the defendant, agreed that, if the ferrule came out, it would be a catastrophe, but he described the relevant practical equation as being a smallish risk. He said it was a commercial risk.

The submission on behalf of the plaintiff said it was not necessary to embark on heavy expenditure, or any particular refinement of engineering knowledge, in order to minimise the risk. There were many simple alternative ways in which the ferrule could be locked, so that the risk of displacement could be removed altogether. In the familiar cases over the past 30 or 40 years, in which the duty of care has been examined in different contexts, it had rightly been held that it is a material consideration to consider how much trouble and how much expense a manufacturer or an employer should have to undertake in order to minimise, or altogether remove, quite a small risk in terms of the incidence of a risk carrying with it the gravity of a major catastrophe in the event of the risk supervening.

Sir Roualeyn Cumming-Bruce said in his judgment

In my view, on the evidence before the judge, she was right to hold that the defendant as a manufacturer was under an obligation to address his mind to the safety of the components that he was proposing to purchase and incorporate and was not entitled blindly to purchase and incorporate such materials and gadgets as Ford or other manufacturers such as Weber were putting on the market.

It was his duty to apply such engineering skill and knowledge as is appropriate to the manufacturer and marketer of a motor car and, on the evidence of the plaintiff's experts which the learned judge accepted, a manufacturer, with a reasonably appropriate degree of knowledge and expertise, should address his mind to the suitability of this particular push fit, relying on different metal components to operate in circumstances of high temperature, and should have considered that there was a problem resulting from a potential gradual developing instability which might, in an appropriate combination of circumstance and forces, ultimately give rise to a displacement in a ferrule during the operation of the engine with an obvious serious risk of fire. There is no evidence that the defendants ever addressed their minds to the risk at all and, on the evidence of Mr Halstead himself, who presented the evidence of the policy of the company, it was open to the judge to hold, as she did, that, when the defendants cast what Mr Halstead described as an engineering eye over the equipment, they were under a duty to observe what Dias described as a clearly retrograde practice. If they had addressed their minds, then, even though the risk was, on the history, obviously a risk of low incidence, they were under a duty to minimize it by some simple device by reason of the gravity of the circumstances that might or would supervene in the event of a ferrule becoming displaced.

The appeal was dismissed.

# CASE HISTORY 20

## Tay Bridge Disaster

In 1870 the North British Railway Company obtained the assent of Parliament to the construction of a bridge two miles long over the estuary of the River Tay. It took six years to build and was the longest bridge in the world when the Government Inspector from the Board of Trade declared the bridge to be safe and fit for use in 1878.

On Sunday 29 December 1879 the 5.27pm train from Burntisland to Dundee was crossing the 1060 yards of the Firth when 13 spans, and the 12 towers that supported them, were carried away. The locomotive, five carriages and a brake van together with 75 men, women and children plunged to their deaths. The storm that night had a ferocity that few had experienced before.

The Board of Trade inquiry examined 120 witnesses and asked 20 000 questions. There was a speed limit of 25 mph on the bridge and the five engine-drivers who gave evidence all denied they had ever exceeded it, or had raced the ferry-boats across the water below. The thirteen high central-spans were supported on towers of six cast iron columns. Each column was built of seven pipes bolted together through their flanges.

The inquiry heard from the workmen at the Wormit Foundry, which had cast the columns, that there was a great lack of what we would call quality control. Blow holes and faults in the castings were filled with Beaumont Egg, which was a mixture of beeswax, fiddler's resin, iron borings and lamp black. Before leaving Wormit's the columns were painted or covered with white lead and grease which disguised the defects.

The bridge had been designed by Sir Thomas Bouch who had asked the advice of the Astronomer Royal on wind pressure, when he was making preliminary plans for a bridge across the Forth. The Astronomer Royal had written in a letter, 'I think we may say the greatest wind pressure to which a plane surface like that of the bridge will be subjected on its whole extent is 10 lb per square foot.'

During the inquiry the Wreck Commissioner asked the designer

> 'Sir Thomas, did you in designing this bridge make any allowance at all for wind pressure?'
> 'Not specially.'
> 'Was there not a particular pressure had in view by you at the time you make the design?'
> 'I had the report of the Forth Bridge.'

Preparations for starting the contract to build the Tay Bridge were well advanced in 1870. The letter from the Astronomer Royal was written in 1873.

The Secretary of the Meteorological Council told the inquiry that the wind pressure down the Tay, along a front of 250 feet, could be more than 50 lb per square foot and the velocity more than 90 mph. After the disaster the Astronomer Royal published a paper on winds and bridges in which he wrote, 'all calculations for the strength of the proposed structure should be based on the assumption of a pressure of 120 lb to the square foot.' He called this 'establishing a modulus of safety'.

The Government Inspector from the Board of Trade did not test the bridge for the effects of wind pressure.

The report of the inquiry blamed Sir Thomas Bouch for the design defects and for failing to supervise the construction of the bridge. Some of the girders from Bouch's bridge were used in the second Tay bridge which was opened in 1887. Today the stumps of old piers can still be seen acting as cutwaters for the new piers.

The locomotive, a 4-4-0 No 224, which pulled the ill-fated train was recovered from the Tay and afterwards worked for 39 years. A Relief Fund was set up to help the families of those who died and the last application for assistance was received in the late 1930s. It was from the sister of one of the two guards who had travelled on that 5.27pm from Burntisland to Dundee.

In December 1985 Professor Iain MacLeod of Strathclyde University said that new research showed that the disaster was the result of poor design, which could not have been avoided by higher standards of construction. Modern analysis techniques revealed that the bolts used in the bridge were not strong enough to hold it in a Force 10 wind.

## SOURCES

Thomas, J (1972) *The Tay Bridge Disaster*. Newton Abbot, David & Charles.

Perkins, J (1975) *The Tay Bridge Disaster*. The City of Dundee District Council.

Prebble, J (1980) *The High Girders*. London, Secker & Warburg.

*The Times* 11 December 1985.

# CASE HISTORY 21

## The Battle of Crecy 1346

The perceptive company will make sure that its designers keep up to date with the state of their particular art. That is to say, the knowledge available to the prudent practitioner who has kept abreast of the latest developments available in his field, especially if he is an acknowledged leading expert. Failure to recognise an advance in the state of the art can have disastrous consequences, from the point of view of the safety of those for whom one is responsible.

Late one Saturday afternoon on a summer day near the end of August, Philip VI of France faced Edward III of England at Crecy, near Abbeville. Philip had about 35 000 men, including 6000 Genoese cross-bowmen, while Edward had about 10 000, of whom 6000 or 7000 were archers with the long-bow who 'shot their arrows with such force and quickness that it seemed as if it snowed'.

It has been estimated that the English long-bowmen fired about 30 volleys totalling some 150 000 arrows in all. The effect of the long-bow was such that the French withdrew at nightfall, having lost about a third of their numbers. The battle of Crecy took place in 1346. But the long-bow was in common use before the fourteenth century, certainly Edward I in the thirteenth century was employing a small number of English archers. The first battle of importance in which the power of the long-bow was felt was that of Falkirk in 1298, when Edward defeated 10 000 Scottish infantrymen and 200 knights with 15 000 Welsh, Cheshire and Lancashire infantrymen. For the next two hundred years it dominated the European battlefield and gave the English superiority in fire power over all her adversaries.

Traditionally the bow was made of yew but also hazel, ash and elm were used. The stave was about six feet long with a diameter of one and a half inches in the centre, with a bow string of flax or linen. The arrows were made of birch, ash or oak and were either lightweight flight arrows or heavy sheaf arrows. Reinforced mail armour was useless at close range for the sheaf arrows could pierce gambeson, mail and aketon, and all too often found their way between or even through the plates of the coat. Arrows from Welsh long-bows had penetrated the door of Abergavenny Castle in the late twelfth century. The door was two inches thick and the heads protruded an inch clear of the door on the inside.

There was nothing new in the state of the art as introduced by Edward to Philip at Crecy. The long-bow brought into the field a yeoman type of soldier with whom there was nothing to compare on the Continent. Philip and the French were ignorant of this development in warfare and, in consequence, paid the penalty of not making sure their design kept up with the state of the art.

# CASE HISTORY 22

## Icarus

In Greek mythology Daedalus built a retreat for King Minos at Cnossus in Crete; it was called the Labyrinth and seemed to have neither beginning nor end, like the river Meander which returns on itself. Daedalus fell out of favour with the king who locked him up in a tower, together with his son Icarus. Minos kept all his ships under military guard so that escape by sea was impossible; but the king could not control the air.

Daedalus was a very skilled craftsman and set to work to make wings for himself and Icarus. He used quill feathers threaded together, with the smaller ones held in place by wax.

When all was ready for the flight the father said, 'My son, be warned! Neither soar too high, lest the sun melt the wax; nor sweep too low, lest the feathers be wetted by the sea.' They flew away from the island; the fishermen, shepherds and ploughmen looking upwards mistook them for gods. They passed Samos and Delos on the left and Lebynthos on the right.

Then Icarus disobeyed his father's warning and began to soar towards the sun. The heat softened the wax, which allowed the feathers it held to come free, and he plunged into the sea and was drowned. Daedalus carried the body to a nearby island which is now called Icaria, and which gave its name to the surrounding sea.

A cursory examination of this case could ascribe Icarus's death to a design defect. But in fact it was caused by his contributory negligence in ignoring a specific product warning. A cost-benefit analysis would show that the benefit of escaping from the clutches of Minos outweighed the risks associated with the only mode that could be used. Daedalus applied the best state of the art available and his design must be judged by the knowledge in Crete at that time. The circumstances of his position were such that the product could not be assessed for development risks, as only one attempt was possible.

Later, Daedulus was able to settle his account with Minos. This he did by fixing a pipe in the roof of a bathroom used by the king. While Minos luxuriated in a warm bath Daedalus poured boiling water upon him down his pipe.

# GLOSSARY

Breach of Warranty

A failure by a party to a contract to satisfy the standard required by a warranty, common law or statutory, express or implied, applicable to that contract. In general a warranty is an undertaking of a non-fundamental nature for the breach of which an action lies, but for which the contract cannot be declared at an end.

Broker, Insurance

An insurance intermediary who advises clients on their insurance requirements and arranges their insurance.

Burden of Proof (onus of proof)

The question of which party to a dispute on a fact must undertake to try to establish the disputed fact.

Captive

An insurance company owned by a company partly or fully to insure the company's risk.

Case Law

The general term for principles and rules of law laid down in judicial decisions, for generalisations based on past decisions of courts and tribunals in particular cases.

Certification

The act of certifying, by means of a certificate of conformity or mark of conformity, that a product or service is in conformity with specific standards or technical specification.

Code of Practice

A document providing practical guidance for the design, manufacture, setting-up, maintenance or utilisation of

|  |  |
|---|---|
|  | equipment, installations, structures or products. |
| Common Law | The royal justices of the English kings developed and administered general rules common to the whole of England, as distinct from the local customs, peculiarities and variations. The common law accordingly came to mean the whole law of England, including ecclesiastical, maritime and mercantile law, as distinct from that of other countries, particularly those based on Roman law. |
| Contract | An agreement between two or more persons intended to create a legal obligation between them to be legally enforceable. |
| Contract Condition | A clause in a contract prescribing an act or event on which the existence or quality or effectiveness of some obligation or payment is dependent. |
| Cut-off | The period after which proceedings against the producer of a defective product may not be instituted. |
| Development Risks | The residual chance that unforeseen failure modes will be revealed in a new product once it has been put on the market. |
| Duty of Care | The legal duty to take reasonable care to avoid acts or omissions which are likely to injure those to whom the duty is owned. Breach of this duty gives rise to liability for negligence. |
| Exemption Clause | One which purports in general terms to limit or exclude the liability of a party which would otherwise arise under a contract. |
| Fundamental Breach | If a party to a contract failed to comply with his fundamental obligations under it, he would not be allowed by the courts to rely on its |

| | |
|---|---|
| | terms, and in particular terms excluding or restricting his liability. |
| Liability, Absolute | In the law of tort liability in damages, imposed by reason of the mere occurrence of the accident of a kind deemed prohibited, without regard to care of precautions taken and without need for proof of negligence or fault. |
| Liability, No-fault | The doctrine that a person who has sustained any stated injuries or losses should have a claim against an injurer or fund, frequently managed by the State, without having to establish that another person was liable for fault in causing him the harm complained of. |
| Liability, Product | The issue of whether, on what basis, and to what extent a manufacturer or supplier of some product should be liable to the ultimate consumer or user for harm done by reason of a defect in design or manufacture. |
| Liability, Strict | The term in the law of tort for a standard of liability which is more stringent than the ordinary one of liability for failure to take reasonable care, yet not absolute, which is the standard sometimes set by statute, where liability arises if the harm to be prevented takes place, whatever care and precautions have been taken. |
| Liability-sensitive | A product, or a company or an industry associated with it, a defect in which can present grave risks to users, eg electrical domestic appliance manufacturer, aerospace, or pork pies. |
| Limitation of Actions | The principle in English law that after the lapse of a fixed period of time an action is not maintainable. |
| Lloyd's (of London) | A section of the insurance market consisting of individual underwriters (and groups of underwriters working in syndicates) each transacting marine |

| | |
|---|---|
| | or non-marine insurance on their own account in the City. For the pedant, Lloyd's is concerned with insurance but Lloyds is the bank. |
| Merchantable quality | Goods of any kind are of merchantable quality if they are as fit for the purpose or purposes for which goods of that kind are commonly bought as it is reasonable to expect, having regard to any description applied to them, the price (if relevant) and all other relevant circumstances. |
| Negligence | In legal usage it signifies the failure to exercise the standard of care which the doer, as a reasonable man should, by law, have exercised in the circumstances. The name negligence is given to a specific kind of tort, the tort of failing in particular circumstances to exercise the care which should have been shown in those circumstances, the care of the reasonable man, and of thereby causing harm to another in person or property. |
| Negligence, Contributory | A partial or complete defence to liability in negligence when it could be shown that the plaintiff was partly or wholly responsible for his injuries. |
| Product Extortion | The crime in which a product, often food or drink, is contaminated and then made available to the public, or threatened to be made available to the public. In return for information regarding the location of the contaminated packs, or abandoning the threat, there is a demand for a consideration: money, the release of prisoners or the wide publication of radical views. Also the threat to contaminate a product. Akin to blackmail. |

| | |
|---|---|
| Product Recall | Generally, the action taken to remove, repair, replace, retrofit or correct a defective product. Putting the distribution chain into reverse. |
| Product Sabotage | The crime in which a product, often food or drink, is contaminated and then made available to the public, or a section of it. There is no demand for consideration or an offer to provide information about the contaminated packs. Can be used to settle a grudge. |
| Quality Assurance | The totality of features and characteristics of a product or service that bear on its ability to satisfy a given need. |
| Quality Control | A system for programming and co-ordinating the efforts of the various groups in an organisation to maintain or improve quality, at an economical level which allows for customer satisfaction. |
| Regulation | A binding document which contains legislative, regulatory or administrative rules and which is adopted and published by an authority legally vested with the necessary power. |
| Reinsurance | The system by which an insurance company or underwriter who has accepted an insurance shares part of the risk with another in the risk with another insurer to lessen his own ultimate liability. The responsibility of the original insurer to the policy-holder for the full amount covered is not in any way affected by such reinsurance. |
| *Res ipsa loquitur* | The thing speaks for itself. A principle often invoked in the law of tort, to the effect that the event itself is indicative of negligence. |

Safety-critical | A component or ingredient which has a significant influence on the overall safety of the end-product in which it is used.

Specification | The document that prescribes in detail the requirements with which the product or service has to comply.

Standard | A technical specification approved by a recognised standardising body for repeated or continuous application.

State of the art | A term applied to the cumulative knowledge and experience of an industry at a given point in time about a specific topic; usually with reference to when a product was made. The scientific and technological knowledge available to the prudent manufacturer.

Tort | The term in common law systems for the civilly actionable harm or wrong, and for the branch of law dealing with liability for such wrongs.

*Uberrimae fidei* | Of the utmost good faith. A term applied to a category of contracts and arrangements where each party must not only refrain from misrepresenting to the other but must voluntarily and positively disclose any factor which a reasonable person in the position of the other party might regard as material in determining whether or not to undertake the contract.

Unavoidably unsafe products | There are some products which in the present state of human knowledge, are quite incapable of being made safe for their intended and ordinary use. Such a product, properly prepared, and accompanied by proper directions and warning, is not defective, nor is it unreasonably dangerous. The seller of such products is not to be held to strict liability for unfortunate

| | |
|---|---|
| | consequences attending their use, merely because he has undertaken to supply the public with an apparently useful and desirable product, attended with a known but apparently reasonable risk (US Restatement of the Law of Torts). |
| Underwriter | In an insurance company, the person who accepts or declines risks and who decides the terms and rates which are acceptable. At Lloyd's a member who accepts risks for his own account as an individual or for a syndicate. |
| Unreasonably dangerous product | The product sold must be dangerous to an extent beyond that which would be contemplated by the ordinary consumer who purchases it, with the ordinary knowledge common to the community as to its characteristics (US Restatement of the Law of Torts). |

# APPENDICES

# CONSUMER PROTECTION ACT 1987

## PART I
## PRODUCT LIABILITY

The EEC Directive on Liability for Defective Products, see Chapter 3 and this Appendix, is implemented by Part I of the Consumer Protection Act 1987, see Chapter 1 for a summary.

**1** (1)  This Part shall have effect for the purpose of making such provision as is necessary in order to comply with the product liability Directive and shall be construed accordingly.

(2)   In this Part, except in so far as the context otherwise requires —

'agricultural produce' means any produce of the soil, of stock-farming or of fisheries;

'dependant' and 'relative' have the same meaning as they have in, respectively, the Fatal Accidents Act 1976 and the Damages (Scotland) Act 1976;

'producer', in relation to a product, means—

a)  the person who manufactured it;

b)  in the case of a substance which has not been manufactured but has been won or abstracted, the person who won or abstracted it;

c)  in the case of a product which has not been manufactured, won or abstracted but essential characteristics of which are attributable to an industrial or other process having been carried out (for example, in relation to agricultural produce), the person who carried out that process;

'product' means any goods or electricity and (subject to subsection (3) below) includes a product which is comprised in another product, whether by virtue of being a component part or raw material or otherwise; and

'the product liability Directive' means the directive of the Council of the European Communities, dated 25 July 1985, (No. 85/374/EEC) on the approximation of the laws, regulations and administrative provisions of the member States concerning liability for defective products.

(3)   For the purposes of this Part a person who supplies any product in which products are comprised, whether by virtue of being component parts or raw materials or otherwise, shall not be treated by reason only of his supply of that product as supplying any of the products so comprised.

**2** (1) Subject to the following provisions of this Part, where any damage is caused wholly or partly by a defect in a product, every person to whom subsection (2) below applies shall be liable for the damage.

Liability for defective products.

(2)   This subsection applies to —

a)   the producer of the product;

b)   any person who, by putting his name on the product or using a trade mark or other distinguishing mark in relation to the product, has held himself out to be the producer of the product;

c)   any person who has imported the product into a member State from a place outside the member States in order, in the course of any business of his, to supply it to another.

(3)   Subject as aforesaid, where any damage is caused wholly or partly by a defect in a product, any person who supplied the product (whether to the person who suffered the damage, to the producer of any product in which the product in question is comprised or to any other person) shall be liable for the damage if —

a)   the person who suffered the damage requests the supplier to identify one or more of the persons (whether still in existence or not) to whom subsection (2) above applies in relation to the product;

b)   that request is made within a reasonable period after the damage occurs and at a time when it is not reasonably practicable for the person making the request to identify all those persons; and

c)  the supplier fails, within a reasonable period after receiving the request, either to comply with the request or to identify the person who supplied the product to him.

(4) Neither subsection (2) nor subsection (3) above shall apply to a person in respect of any defect in any game or agricultural produce if the only supply of the game or produce by that person to another was at a time when it had not undergone an industrial process.

(5) Where two or more persons are liable by virtue of this Part for the same damage, their liability shall be joint and several.

(6) This section shall be without prejudice to any liability arising otherwise than by virtue of this Part.

Meaning of 'defect'.

**3** (1) Subject to the following provisions of this section, there is a defect in a product for the purposes of this Part if the safety of the product is not such as persons generally are entitled to expect; and for those purposes 'safety', in relation to a product, shall include safety with respect to products comprised in that product and safety in the context of risks of damage to property, as well as in the context of risks of death or personal injury.

(2) In determining for the purposes of subsection (1) above what persons generally are entitled to expect in relation to a product all the circumstances shall be taken into account, include —

a)  the manner in which, and purposes for which, the product has been marketed, its get-up, the use of any mark in relation to the product and any instructions for, or warnings with respect to, doing or refraining from doing anything with or in relation to the product;

(b) what might reasonably be expected to be done with or in relation to the product; and

(c) the time when the product was supplied by its producer to another;

and nothing in this section shall require a defect to be inferred from the fact alone that the safety of a product which is supplied after that time is greater than the safety of the product in question.

**4** (1) In any civil proceedings by virtue of this Part against any person ('the person proceeded against') in respect of a defect in a product it shall be a defence for him to show —

a) that the defect is attributable to compliance with any requirement imposed by or under any enactment or with any Community obligation; or

b) that the person proceeded against did not at any time supply the product to another; or

c) that the following conditions are satisfied, that is to say—

i) that the only supply of the product to another by the person proceeded against was otherwise than in the course of a business of that person's; and

ii) that section 2(2) above does not apply to that person or applies to him by virtue only of things done otherwise than with a view to profit; or

d) that the defect did not exist in the product at the relevant time; or

e) that the state of scientific and technical

knowledge at the relevant time was not such that a producer of products of the same description as the product in question might be expected to have discovered the defect if it had existed in his products while they were under his control; or

f)   that the defect—

i) constituted a defect in a product ('the subsequent product') in which the product in question had been comprised; and

ii) was wholly attributable to the design of the subsequent product or to compliance by the producer of the product in question with instructions given by the producer of the subsequent product.

(2) In this section 'the relevant time', in relation to electricity, means the time at which it was generated, being a time before it was transmitted or distributed, and in relation to any other product, means —

a) if the person proceeded against is a person to whom subsection (2) of section 2 above applies in relation to the product, the time when he supplied the product to another;

b) if that subsection does not apply to that person in relation to the product, the time when the product was last supplied by a person to whom that subsection does apply in relation to the product.

Damage giving rise to liability.

5 (1) Subject to the following provisions of this section, in this Part 'damage' means death or personal injury or any loss of or damage to any property (including land).

(2) A person shall not be liable under section 2 above in respect of any defect in a

product for the loss of or any damage to the product itself or for the loss of or any damage to the whole or any part of any product which has been supplied with the product in question comprised in it.

(3) A person shall not be liable under section 2 above for any loss of or damage to any property which, at the time it is lost or damaged, is not —

a) of a description of property ordinarily intended for private use, occupation or consumption; and

b) intended by the person suffering the loss or damage mainly for his own private use, occupation or consumption.

(4) No damages shall be awarded to any person by virtue of this Part in respect of any loss of or damage to any property if the amount which would fall to be so awarded to that person, apart from this subsection and any liability for interest, does not exceed £275.

(5) In determining for the purposes of this Part who has suffered any loss of or damage to property and when any such loss or damage occurred, the loss or damage shall be regarded as having occurred at the earliest time at which a person with an interest in the property had knowledge of the material facts about the loss or damage.

(6) For the purposes of subsection (5) above the material facts about any loss of or damage to any property are such facts about the loss or damage as would lead a reasonable person with an interest in the property to consider the loss or damage sufficiently serious to justify his instituting proceedings for damages against a defendant who did not dispute liability and was able to satisfy a judgment.

(7) For the purposes of subsection (5) above a person's knowledge includes knowledge which he might reasonably have been expected to acquire —

(a) from facts observable or ascertainable by him; or

(b) from facts ascertainable by him with the help of appropriate expert advice which it is reasonable for him to seek;

but a person shall not be taken by virtue of this subsection to have knowledge of a fact ascertainable by him only with the help of expert advice unless he has failed to take all reasonable steps to obtain (and, where appropriate, to act on) that advice.

(8) Subsections (5) to (7) above shall not extend to Scotland.

Application of certain enactments etc.

**6** (1) Any damage for which a person is liable under section 2 above shall be deemed to have been caused —

1976 c. 30.

a) for the purposes of the Fatal Accidents Act 1976, by that person's wrongful act, neglect or default;

1940 c. 42.

b) for the purposes of section 3 of the Law Reform (Miscellaneous Provisions) (Scotland) Act 1940 (contribution among joint wrongdoers), by that person's wrongful act or negligent act or omission;

1976 c. 13.

c) for the purposes of section 1 of the Damages (Scotland) Act 1976 (rights of relatives of a deceased), by that person's act or omission; and

1982 c. 53.

d) for the purposes of Part II of the Administration of Justice Act 1982 (damages for personal injuries, etc. — Scotland), by an act or omission giving rise to liability in that person to pay damages.

(2) Where —

a) a person's death is caused wholly or partly by a defect in a product, or a person dies after suffering damage which has been so caused;

b) a request such as mentioned in paragraph (a) of subsection (3) of section 2 above is made to a supplier of the product by that person's personal representatives or, in the case of a person whose death is caused wholly or partly by the defect, by any dependant or relative of that person; and

c) the conditions specified in paragraphs (b) and (c) of that subsection are satisfied in relation to that request,

this Part shall have effect for the purposes of the Law Reform (Miscellaneous Provisions) Act 1934, the Fatal Accidents Act 1976 and the Damages (Scotland) Act 1976 as if liability of the supplier to that person under that subsection did not depend on that person having requested the supplier to identify certain persons or on the said conditions having been satisfied in relation to a request made by that person.
1934 c. 41.

(3) Section 1 of the Congenital Disabilities (Civil Liability) Act 1976 shall have effect for the purposes of this Part as if —
1976 c. 28.

a) a person were answerable to a child in respect of an occurrence caused wholly or partly by a defect in a product if he is or has been liable under secion 2 above in respect of any effect of the occurrence on a parent of the child, or would be so liable if the occurrence caused a parent of the child to suffer damage;

b) the provisions of this Part relating to liability under section 2 above applied in relation to liability by virtue of paragraph (a) above under the said section 1; and

PART I

c) subsection (6) of the said section 1 (exclusion of liability) were omitted.

(4) Where any damage is caused partly by a defect in a product and partly by the fault of the person suffering the damage, the Law Reform (Contributory Negligence) Act 1945 and section 5 of the Fatal Accidents Act 1976 (contributory negligence) shall have effect as if the defect were the fault of every person liable by virtue of this Part for the damage caused by the defect.

1945 c. 28.
1976 c. 30.

(5) In subsection (4) above 'fault' has the same meaning as in the said Act of 1945.

(6) Schedule 1 to this Act shall have the effect for the purpose of amending the Limitation Act 1980 and the Prescription and Limitation (Scotland) Act 1973 in their application in relation to the bringing of actions by virtue of this Part.

1980 c. 58.
1973 c. 52.

(7) It is hereby declared that liability by virtue of this Part is to be treated as liability in tort for the purposes of any enactment conferring jurisdiction on any court with respect to any matter.

(8) Nothing in this Part shall prejudice the operation of section 12 of the Nuclear Installations Act 1965 (rights to compensation for certain breaches of duties confined to rights under that Act).

1965 c. 57

Prohibition on exclusions from liability.

7 The liability of a person by virtue of this Part to a person who has suffered damage caused wholly or partly by a defect in a product, or to a dependant or relative of such a person, shall not be limited or excluded by any contract term, by any notice or by any other provision.

Power to modify Part I.

8 (1) Her Majesty may by Order in Council make such modifications of this Part and of any other enactment (including an enactment contained in the following Parts of this Act, or in

an Act passed after this Act) as appear to Her Majesty in Council to be necessary or expedient in consequence of any modification of the product liability Directive which is made at any time after the passing of the Act.

(2) An Order in Council under subsection (1) above shall not be submitted to Her Majesty in Council unless a draft of the Order has been laid before, and approved by a resolution of, each House of Parliament.

**9** (1) Subject to subsection (2) below, this Part shall bind the Crown.

(2) The Crown shall not, as regards the Crown's liability by virtue of this Part, be bound by this Part further than the Crown is made liable in tort or in reparation under the Crown Proceedings Act 1947, as that Act has effect from time to time.

PART I

Application of Part I to Crown.

1947 c. 44.

# EEC DIRECTIVE ON LIABILITY FOR DEFECTIVE PRODUCTS

## Council Directive

## of 25 July 1985

on the approximation of the laws, regulations and administrative provisions of the Member States concerning liability for defective products
(85/374/EEC)

THE COUNCIL OF THE EUROPEAN COMMUNITIES,

Having regard to the Treaty establishing the European Economic Community, and in particular Article 100 thereof,

Having regard to the proposal from the Commission [1],

Having regard to the opinion of the European Parliament [2],

Having regard to the opinion of the Economic and Social Committee [3],

Whereas approximation of the laws of the Member States concerning the liability of the producer for damage caused by the defectiveness of his products is necessary because the existing divergences may distort competition and affect the movement of goods within the common market and entail a differing degree of protection of the consumer against damage caused by a defective product to his health or property;

Whereas liability without fault on the part of the producer is the sole means of adequately solving the problem, peculiar to our age of increasing technicality, of a fair apportionment of the risks inherent in modern technological production;

Whereas liability without fault should apply only to movables which have been industrially produced; whereas, as a result, it is

---

[1] OJ No C 241, 14. 10. 1976, p. 9 and OJ No C 271, 26. 10. 1979, p. 3.

[2] OJ No C 127, 21. 5. 1979, p. 61.

[3] OJ No C 114, 7. 5. 1979, p. 15.

appropriate to exclude liability for agricultural products and game, except where they have undergone a processing of an industrial nature which could cause a defect in these products; whereas the liability provided for in this Directive should also apply to movables which are used in the construction of immovables or are installed in immovables;

Whereas protection of the consumer requires that all producers involved in the production process should be made liable, in so far as their finished product, component part or any raw material supplied by them was defective; whereas, for the same reason, liability should extend to importers of products into the Community and to persons who present themselves as producers by affixing their name, trade mark or other distinguishing feature or who supply a product the producer of which cannot be identified;

Whereas, in situations where several persons are liable for the same damage, the protection of the consumer requires that the injured person should be able to claim full compensation for the damge from any one of them;

Whereas, to protect the physical well-being and property of the consumer, the defectiveness of the product should be determined by reference not to its fitness for use but to the lack of the safety which the public at large is entitled to expect; whereas the safety is assessed by excluding any misuse of the product not reasonable under the circumstances;

Whereas a fair apportionment of risk between the injured person and the producer implies that the producer should be able to free himself from liability if he furnishes proof as to the existence of certain exonerating circumstances;

Whereas the protection of the consumer requires that the liability of the producer remains unaffected by acts or omissions of other persons having contributed to cause the damage; whereas, however, the contributory negligence of the injured person may be taken into account to reduce or disallow such liability;

Whereas the protection of the consumer requires compensation for death and personal injury as well as compensation for damage to property; whereas the latter should nevertheless be limited to goods for private use or consumption and be subject to a deduction of a lower threshold of a fixed amount in order to avoid litigation in an excessive number of cases; whereas this Directive should not prejudice compensation for pain and suffering and other non-material damages payable, where appropriate, under the law applicable to the case;

Whereas a uniform period of limitation for the bringing of action for compensation is in the interests both of the injured person and of the producer;

Whereas products age in the course of time, higher safety standards are developed and the state of science and technology progresses; whereas, therefore, it would not be reasonable to make the producer liable for an unlimited period for the defectiveness of his product; whereas, therefore, liability should expire after a reasonable length of time, without prejudice to claims pending at law;

Whereas, to achieve effective protection of consumers, no contractual derogation should be permitted as regards the liability of the producer in relation to the injured person;

Whereas under the legal systems of the Member States an injured party may have a claim for damages based on grounds of contractual liability or on grounds of non-contractual liability other than that provided for in this Directive; in so far as these provisions also serve to attain the objective of effective protection of consumers, they should remain unaffected by this Directive; whereas, in so far as effective protection of consumers in the sector of pharmaceutical products is already also attained in a Member State under a special liability system, claims based on this system should similarly remain possible;

Whereas, to the extent that liability for nuclear injury or damage is already covered in all Member States by adequate special rules, it has been possible to exclude damage of this type from the scope of this Directive;

Whereas, since the exclusion of primary agricultural products and game from the scope of this Directive may be felt, in certain Member States, in view of what is expected for the protection of consumers, to restrict unduly such protection, it should be possible for a Member State to extend liability to such products;

Whereas, for similar reasons, the possibility offered to a producer to free himself from liability if he proves that the state of scientific and technical knowledge at the time when he put the product into circulation was not such as to enable the existence of a defect to be discovered may be felt in certain Member States to restrict unduly the protection of the consumer; whereas it should therefore be possible for a Member State to maintain in its legislation or to provide by new legislation that this exonerating circumstance is not admitted, whereas, in the case of new legislation, making use of this derogation should, however, be subject to a Community stand-still procedure, in order to raise, if possible, the level of protection in a uniform manner throughout the Community;

Whereas, taking into account the legal traditions in most of the Member States, it is inappropriate to set any financial ceiling on the producer's liability without fault; whereas, in so far as there are, however, differing traditions, it seems possible to admit that a Member State may derogate from the principle of unlimited liability by providing a limit for the total liability of the producer for damage resulting from a death or personal injury and caused by identical items with the same defect, provided that this limit is established at a level sufficiently high to guarantee adequate protection of the consumer and the correct functioning of the common market;

Whereas the harmonisation resulting from this cannot be total at the present stage, but opens the way towards greater harmonisation; whereas it is therefore necessary that the Council receive at regular intervals, reports from the Commission on the application of this Directive, accompanied, as the case may be, by appropriate proposals;

Whereas it is particularly important in this respect that a re-examination be carried out of those parts of the Directive relating to the derogations open to the Member States, at the expiry of a period of sufficient length to gather practical experience on the effects of these derogations on the protection of consumers and on the functioning of the common market,

## HAS ADOPTED THIS DIRECTIVE:

### Article 1
The producer shall be liable for damage caused by a defect in his product.

### Article 2
For the purpose of this Directive 'product' means all movables,

with the exception of primary agricultural products and game, even though incorporated into another movable or into an immovable. 'Primary agricultural products' means the products of the soil, of stock-farming and of fisheries, excluding products which have undergone initial processing. 'Product' includes electricity.

## Article 3

1.    'Producer' means the manufacturer of a finished product, the producer of any raw material or the manufacturer of a component part and any person who, by putting his name, trade mark or other distinguishing feature on the product presents himself as its producer.

2.    Without prejudice to the liability of the producer, any person who imports into the Community a product for sale, hire, leasing or any form of distribution in the course of his business shall be deemed to be a producer within the meaning of this Directive and shall be responsible as a producer.

3.    Where the producer of the product cannot be identified, each supplier of the product shall be treated as its producer unless he informs the injured person, within a reasonable time, of the identity of the producer or of the person who supplied him with the product. The same shall apply, in the case of an imported product, if this product does not indicate the identity of the importer referred to in paragraph 2, even if the name of the producer is indicated.

## Article 4

The injured person shall be required to prove the damage, the defect and the causal relationship between defect and damage.

## Article 5

Where, as a result of the provisions of this Directive, two or more persons are liable for the same damage, they shall be liable jointly and severally, without prejudice to the provisions of national law concerning the rights of contribution or recourse.

## Article 6

1.    A product is defective when it does not provide the safety which a person is entitled to expect, taking all circumstances into account, including:

a)    the presentation of the product;

b)    the use to which it could reasonably be expected that the product would be put;

c)      the time when the product was put into circulation.

2.      A product shall not be considered defective for the sole reason that a better product is subsequently put into circulation.

### *Article 7*

The producer shall not be liable as a result of this Directive if he proves:

a)      that he did not put the product into circulation; or

b)      that, having regard to the circumstances, it is probable that the defect which caused the damage did not exist at the time when the product was put into circulation by him or that this defect came into being afterwards; or

c)      that the product was neither manufactured by him for sale or any form of distribution for economic purpose nor manufactured or distributed by him in the course of his business; or

d)      that the defect is due to compliance of the product with mandatory regulations issued by the public authorities; or

e)      that the state of scientific and technical knowledge at the time when he put the product into circulation was not such as to enable the existence of the defect to be discovered; or

f)      in the case of a manufacturer of a component, that the defect is attributable to the design of the product in which the component has been fitted or to the instructions given by the manufacturer of the product.

### *Article 8*

1.      Without prejudice to the provisions of national law concerning the right of contribution or recourse, the liability of the producer shall not be reduced when the damage is caused both by a defect in product and by the act or omission of a third party.

2.      The liability of the producer may be reduced or disallowed when, having regard to all the circumstances, the damage is caused both by a defect in the product and by the fault of the injured person or any person for whom the injured person is responsible.

*Article 9*

For the purpose of Article 1, 'damage' means:

a)      damage caused by death or by personal injuries;

b)      damage to, or destruction of, any item of property other than the defective product itself, with a lower threshold of 500 ECU, provided that the item of property:

  i) is of a type ordinarily intended for private use or consumption, and

  ii) was used by the injured person mainly for his own private use or consumption.

This Article shall be without prejudice to national provisions relating to non-material damage.

*Article 10*

1.      Member States shall provide in their legislation that a limitation period of three years shall apply to proceedings for the recovery of damages as provided for in this Directive. The limitation period shall begin to run from the day on which the plaintiff became aware, or should reasonably have become aware, of the damage, the defect and the identity of the producer.

2.      The laws of Member States regulating suspension or interruption of the limitation period shall not be affected by this Directive.

*Article 11*

Member States shall provide in their legislation that the rights conferred upon the injured person pursuant to this Directive shall be extinguished upon the expiry of a period of 10 years from the date on which the producer put into circulation the actual product which caused the damage, unless the injured person has in the meantime instituted proceedings against the producer.

*Article 12*

The liability of the producer arising from this Directive may not, in relation to the injured person, be limited or excluded by a provision limiting his liability or exempting him from liability.

*Article 13*

This Directive shall not affect any rights which an injured person may have according to the rules of the law of contractual or non-contractual liability or a special liability system existing at the moment when this Directive is notified.

## Article 14

This Directive shall not apply to injury or damage arising from nuclear accidents and covered by international conventions ratified by the Member States.

## Article 15

1.    Each Member State may:

a)    by way of derogation from Article 2, provide in its legislation that within the meaning of Article 1 of this Directive 'product' also means primary agricultural products and game;

b)    by way of derogation from Article 7 (e), maintain or, subject to the procedure set out in paragraph 2 of this Article, provide in this legislation that the producer shall be liable even if he proves that the state of scientific and technical knowledge at the time when he put the product into circulation was not such as to enable the existence of a defect to be discovered.

2.    A Member State wishing to introduce the measure specified in paragraph 1 (b) shall communicate the text of the proposed measure to the Commission. The Commission shall inform the other Member States thereof.

The Member State concerned shall hold the proposed measure in abeyance for nine months after the Commission is informed and provided that in the meantime the Commission has not submitted to the Council a proposal amending this Directive on the relevant matter. However, if within three months of receiving the said information, the Commission does not advise the Member State concerned that it intends submitting such a proposal to the Council, the Member State may take the proposed measure immediately.

If the Commission does submit to the Council such a proposal amending this Directive within the aforementioned nine months, the Member State concerned shall hold the proposed measure in abeyance for a further period of 18 months from the date on which the proposal is submitted.

3.    Ten years after the date of notification of this Directive, the Commission shall submit to the Council a report on the

effect that rulings by the courts as to the application of Article 7 (e) and of paragraph 1 (b) of this Article have on consumer protection and the functioning of the common market. In the light of this report the Council, acting on a proposal from the Commission and pursuant to the terms of Article 100 of the Treaty, shall decide whether to repeal Article 7 (e).

## Article 16

1.     Any Member State may provide that a producer's total liability for damage resulting from a death or personal injury and caused by identical items with the same defect shall be limited to an amount which may not be less than 70 million ECU.

2.     Ten years after the date of notification of this Directive, the Commission shall submit to the Council a report on the effect on consumer protection and the functioning of the common market of the implementation of the financial limit on liability by those Member States which have used the option provided for in paragraph 1. In the light of this report the Council, acting on a proposal from the Commission and pursuant to the terms of Article 100 of the Treaty, shall decide whether to repeal paragraph 1.

## Article 17

This Directive shall not apply to products put into circulation before the date on which the provisions referred to in Article 19 enter into force.

## Article 18

1.     For the purposes of this Directive, the ECU shall be that defined by Regulation (EEC) No 3180/78 [1], as amended by Regulation (EEC) No 2626/84 [2]. The equivalent in national currency shall initially be calculated at the rate obtaining on the date of adoption of this Directive.

2.     Every five years the Council, acting on a proposal from the Commission, shall examine and, if need be, revise the amounts in this Directive, in the light of economic and monetary trends in the Community.

---

[1] OJ No L 379, 30. 12. 1978, p. 1.

[2] OJ No L 247, 16. 9. 1984, p. 1.

*Article 19*

1.     Member States shall bring into force, not later than three years from the date of notification of this Directive, the laws, regulations and administrative provisions necessary to comply with this Directive. They shall forthwith inform the Commission thereof [1].

2.     The procedure set out in Article 15 (2) shall apply from the date of notification of this Directive.

*Article 20*

Member States shall communicate to the Commission the texts of the main provisions of national law which they subsequently adopt in the field governed by this Directive.

*Article 21*

Every five years the Commission shall present a report to the Council on the application of this Directive and, if necessary, shall submit appropriate proposals to it.

*Article 22*

This Directive is addressed to the Member States.

Done at Brussels, 25 July 1985.

*For the Council*
*The President*
J. Poos

## SOURCE

*Official Journal of the European Communities*, 7 August 1985, pp 22-33.

---

[1] This Directive was notified to the Member States on 30 July 1985.

# INDEX